Introduction

My story of building a swimming pond happened at a low point in my general well-being. I was unfit, overweight and unable to pull myself out of my run-down situation because I was conditioned to the idea that there is a certain way of doing things and that any other way was somehow bad, unrealistic, or plain *wrong*.

As I continued down this familiar track my situation worsened. My tale is not spectacular. Others have negotiated far worse; cancers, personal tragedies, life-changing accidents and more, but there comes a time when each story needs to be heard and sometimes new methods have to be tried.

Building a swimming pond without knowing if it would work while being mildly ridiculed at the audacity of attempting such a thing, coincided with my physical recovery. What ensued was a madcap journey to find a way to heal and, importantly, to remain well. This echoed neatly with building a pool that was so wholly different to the usual offering and completely out of my comfort zone.

These two themes zig-zagged until completion, and have taught me lesson after lesson.

When I started this project, organic pools—or swimming ponds—existed on a tiny scale. There was no easy alternative to the standard, chlorine-filled swimming pool. And people will say 'but chlorine isn't that bad for you, we've been swimming in it for years'. I'd argue that chlorine probably isn't that good for you. Chlorine is basically mild bleach. And there are large red warning signs on bottles of bleach. In any event, I had a dream to swim in something beautiful and natural. I just had no idea how.

Turns out that this meant rethinking an old model and not fearing the repercussions. This ties in with what I discovered about health. I want to make it clear that I have a huge amount of respect for the medical profession who have patched me up brilliantly over my fifty years. What I've learnt is that with more understanding, there are many times when I should never have been there in the first place.

We desperately need to take personal responsibility for our health. If each one of us starts working on ourselves, then the collective becomes fitter and the world instantly becomes less toxic. Only then will humans truly shine, as they ought.

I believe it requires us to turn away from our current domineering, top-down, outsourcing approach where the tentacles and suckers of industry digs ever deeper into our minds and pockets.

I stumbled upon and tried several 'health' methods before discovering a simple routine which transformed my way of life. Of course, my way may not be your way—everyone has their own sweet-spot—but if my small book provides an ounce of inspiration to anyone wishing to seek out a positive and healthy balance in their lives while rekindling the spirit within, then my experiences and this short tale will have been worth it.

You'll also learn how not to build a swimming pond.

* * *

All the following really happened.

On a personal level, some of it is pretty embarrassing and includes moments of great incompetence. It's warts and all, so my apologies in advance.

It also comes with a degree of fortitude, great stubbornness and many trials. There were laughs, triumphs, failures and injuries that occurred over the duration of this book (as you will find out) but at the end there was a pond filled with love.

Relocation and Roads

I'm staring at a pile of bent metal and I really don't know what to do next. In my haste to erect an eight-sleeper Bell tent, nearly all my metal tent-pegs now bend at a strange angle, some nearing ninety degrees, and most are beyond bashing out.

The tent is old and its conical sides are yellowing like a Saharan camel. There's a separate plastic ground sheet and I've stitched this to the sides with an old rope to keep the whole thing together while I attempt to knock the five remaining usable industrial pegs into the ground.

If a storm swings across the fields, and the weatherman says this is likely, the wind will almost certainly pick up the entire structure and drop it into a distant hedge somewhere in North Essex. And since I cannot anchor the fly lines, the tent flaps from side to side, and up and down like a semi-deflated beach ball. Despite my considerable efforts, the tent lacks rigidity. Here on the shallow hill above the Stour Valley in this semi-exposed site, the chances of this tent remaining here by dark are minimal.

Charlotte, my wife, asks why I've bent six pegs beyond repair and I reply that the ground is bone hard and the pegs aren't strong enough. She looks at me as if I'm lying, but she knows I've put this tent up many times before. I ask her to try. She crashes the mallet down with the same result. We now have four usable pegs. I feel vindicated, but she gives me a look as if to say, "Do something about it".

It's now just over a year since we moved from North Yorkshire to North Essex and the experience feels as if we're still finding our feet in a foreign country.

I've returned to my roots, close to my parents, and I've dragged Charlotte and our three kids along. We've moved from the breathtaking views from Sutton Bank across the Vale of York, to a shallower landscape that looks out over the Stour Valley towards Suffolk.

We've swapped the wide, pot-hole-free roads of the North for kamikaze lanes, riddled with bumps, twisting corners and giant craters. These rural lanes are barely wide enough for an Amazon delivery van and they all drive too fast.

Charlotte misses Yorkshire's wide, smooth roads. Navigating our tiny, tree-covered lanes sends her into a panic and even though she's been driving for twenty years, it appears no one taught her how to reverse. Around here it's a must-have skill.

Her tactic when meeting other cars is to examine her fingernails, which she can do for an incredibly long time. This is a stand-off she wins every time. Now, when our neighbours see her car, they instantly back up.

The kids miss their friends and the bedrooms they grew up in.

"You'll get used to it," I say, repeatedly. "And it's so much warmer here and far closer to London," I add, knowing that one day they might thank me. At the moment, the relocation hasn't gone quite as smoothly as I would have hoped. For me, the joy is to be surrounded by open fields, though I know Charlotte feels a little isolated after North Yorkshire village life.

North Yorkshire versus North Essex is like comparing a chocolate biscuit to a doughnut. One is hard, dramatic and crunchy and full of rich flavours. The other is softer, a little more bland and slightly sugary. But there's a subtlety here in North Essex; perhaps it's the sweetness of the jam hidden deep inside.

Anyway, I'm still baffled why the ground is so darned hard. That evening, I drop round to see our neighbour, Henry, a red-faced, rotund man with wispy, slicked-back hair and kind eyes. As we lean over our gates across the tiny lane that separates our properties, he tells me that the area in question used to be a busy farmyard with an eighteenth-century, Grade II listed, timber-clad threshing barn which gradually deteriorated. Eventually, it blew down in a gale.

I listen to Henry's story on the demise of the barn and he tells me about an inventor called Bill, who lived here. Bill created one machine that smashed damaged roads into smithereens and another that heated tarmac and rolled the road smoothly back together again. It sounds like a tarmac version of Humpty Dumpty.

One day, so the story goes, having made millions with these clever road-breaker-fixers, a Japanese multinational company pinched his idea and from that moment forth, he spent the rest of his life in litigation; not for the money, but on the principle.

As I grew up a couple of fields from where we are now, I

remember Bill. As a teenager, we'd sneak down to the Lamarsh Lion pub, where he would occupy a stool in the corner, sipping quietly on his pint of IPA. We knew he was an inventor, so we'd buy him pints hoping that after some sharp questions he'd spill a gem of an invention, which we'd steal, and make a pile of cash. Of course, this never happened. Bill had a terrible stutter and, conversely, the more inebriated he got, the worse his impediment became. We never had the patience to listen to him.

Windynook, his tiny, black, boarded timber hovel (built in the Second World War for the land-girls) ended up swamped by brambles. Inside was a mud floor and next to the kitchen table grew an ash tree that poked straight through the roof. Outside, in the mud, stood a Rolls Royce and a Range Rover.

Bill, Henry tells me, threatened to shoot him with a shotgun over an altercation with their shared water bill and a genuinely terrified Henry had to call in the police on several occasions. Bill's life hadn't ended so well.

Henry implies I haven't got a hope in hell of doing anything with the derelict farmyard and offers me some advice: plant more trees now.

He's got a point. Aside from the tall ash and oak trees that line the long ancient ditch-pond which runs down one side of our garden, we have a solitary tree. It's a small, eight-foot oak.

"They'll get their roots down in ten to fifteen years," he tells me. "It's the wretched clay and flint on this land. I guarantee they'll only just get going when you decide to leave." I note that his trees have only just got going and I wonder if they're about to downsize.

The land-girls' shack was demolished and much to everyone's surprise, a property developer called George erected a large faux-barn conversion about eight times the size of the original footprint. I met George, a doppelgänger of George W. Bush, when he landed his helicopter in the field opposite shortly after we'd moved in. Our kids lined up by the fence and waved wildly at his chopper, a scene which reminded me of that famous moment in the film 'The Railway Children'.

Anyway, the house suits us perfectly, although Henry tells me he did everything in his power to scupper its erection, including reducing the bathroom windows, which is now rather annoying. When he looks across the road, his face crumples at how George was able to build this strange-looking barn so close to his grade-two listed cottage.

He shrugs, gives me a friendly smile and returns to tending his garden. The time he spends outdoors makes me look housebound, but as a consequence, his garden is filled with bulbs and roses and a multitude of pretty shrubs. I know Charlotte is desperate for something similar.

Henry's explanation marries up perfectly with the ninety square metre area at the top end of our property. It's home to an occasional clump of grass and stray patches of moss. And there's one spindly thorn bush poking out. Even brambles can't be bothered to get stuck in and it strikes me that if no super-weeds have found a morsel of goodness to slip a root into, then what on earth is under here? The only benefit I can think of is that it is maintenance free.

I'm beginning to wonder if this isn't really a garden after all.

* * *

For the first time in our married life, I'm working from home, so we've had to configure our days to maintain a harmonious household. There are tensions, petty ones mainly, about who does what, but we keep tight-lipped and I help Charlotte with the kids as much as I can.

On the property, there are endless things to do, like changing the strange bend in the driveway and insulating the garage, which we converted into the world's coldest and therefore most under-used playroom in England. But as we settle in to our new home, I suspect that in order to make this really *our* house, perhaps it needs something we can all enjoy. Something special.

It's my twin brother Ed's throwaway line that gets me thinking. Ed's a garden designer and has a gift that he can look at a god-awful pile of ground and, by suggesting just a few things, can utterly transform a space. And then you wonder why you never thought of it before.

We've strolled down to the end of the garden for a sneaky cigarette and I whine about the uselessness of having an old farmyard as a garden. As we smoke, we stare at the desolate site and I pick up odd fragments of brick and toss them into the ditch pond. He looks about and says, as though it's an incredibly straightforward thing to do.

"Why don't you dig a pond?"

"Seriously, Ed? Why?"

I'm not sure if he's joking, but he grabs a large metal pole-driver and crashes it repeatedly into the ground. He unearths tarmac and stone, odd pieces of farm metal, and endless fragments of brick.

"Bro," he says, sincerely, "what else are you going to do with it?"

* * *

The early summer scene here is a picture; a setting sun right in front of us, a lustrous lawn filled with white daisy heads, and the trees and hedgerow around the ditch-pond are awash with birdsong and late blossom.

I chew on Ed's pond idea, and, as we sit outside on our yellow, riven patio and sip our first glass of rosé for the year, I casually float it past Charlotte.

I'm taken aback by her immediate enthusiasm, but reckon it may have something to do with the wine. We take a stroll towards the old farm yard area following the track beside the ditch-pond. On the way, I stop and stare at something lying in front of us. When Charlotte realises what it is, she attempts to jump on my back and screams so loudly the birdsong ceases and a flock of pigeons thrash out of the trees. Then she runs off in a blind panic.

A one and a half metre long grass snake glances at me unimpressed, and slithers coolly into the long grass and scrub beside the ditch. The last time I saw one of these was when I was a little boy. They're rare and I feel a sense of privilege, but Charlotte is about to phone the estate agent and put the house on the market. I find it curious how a girl brought up on a farm seems to have such a vacuum in understanding the 'natural world'.

The weather remains hot and balmy for the time of year. A week later, we invite a similarly new family to the area for Sunday lunch. The kids play and the adults lie on the lawn in front of the patio, drinking wine and relating stories about our kids while finding out things we have in common. The conversation moves on to what we'd like to do with our new homes.

I mention the idea of digging a pond. It's met with a muted response. When Charlotte says, in the haze of summer rosé, that the area really should be a swimming pool, everyone agrees that's a great idea.

Thing is, I really don't want a swimming pool. I know how much maintenance they need, how much the heating costs, then there's the plant room and changing rooms and so much more. I know I won't get close to affording it.

As I take them up the track to see the wasteland, Charlotte breaks the news that our neighbour across the road has just put their house on the market.

This not-unexpected news reminds me to think about planting some trees.

Lifestyle and David's Pond

The unusually hot weather breaks at the end of April, and in the regular downpours that follow, the pond idea seems miles away. However, I make a few enquiries and find out that a basic swimming pool, with tiles, pump house, covers, plant for heating and filtration—let alone landscaping, comes in at least four times over the price we've earmarked. When I tell Charlotte I can read the disappointment on her face. There's a part of her that wants something flashy and fun so she can keep up with the Joneses. I get that.

I'm curious to know if it's possible to make a pond that one can swim in. I don't even know if such a thing exists—unless, of course, it's a lake where the wind across the water creates movement so the water doesn't stagnate. My father tells me that everyone used to swim in natural pools or rivers when he was a child and when I search deeper, it turns out that there are *swimming ponds*, or *organic pools,* which are expansive, lustrous things with glorious landscaping. Most of these are in Austria, or in Germany and look like beautiful works of art.

Then, online, I discover a guy called David. He lives two hours away, near Norwich, and claims that you can self-build a proper working swimming pond for a fraction of the cost of an ordinary swimming pool. This grabs my attention.

In his videos, David has a friendly face, with ruddy cheeks, enormous glasses and a grey mop of hair that looks like it needs a good wash and trim. He talks with a sliding Merseyside accent and displays an orchestrated, yet charming, sense of disorganisation. With a teeny bit of research, I discover he was a BBC correspondent for the area, and this shows by the way he works the camera. His videos captivate me.

I'm sceptical, but I'm sucked in and purchase his full video and DIY pond-building manual. When it arrives, I play the video over twice. I'm fascinated by the concept and his pond is precisely what I've got in mind. Charlotte looks on over my shoulder for a few minutes before declaring that I've completely lost the plot.

"There's absolutely no way *you* could build that," she says, scanning my large torso.

I am not in a great physical shape. I've put on a lot of weight since I rowed the English Channel a couple of years ago. Then, I was super-fit, but it soon goes if you don't keep it up.

My belly hangs over my belt, and I've recently noticed my overtly fleshy neck. It's not an impressive look. Recently, I had to buy two new pairs of trousers and a couple of XL shirts. Charlotte is not shy about telling me I need to do something about it, generally with blunt language. It's a sign she's worried about me. It's when my children call me "fatty" that I know I've got a problem.

I'm quick to blame this on my knees. Recently, they've been killing me. A couple of years back, I had two meniscus operations, one on each knee. This removes fragments of loose cartilage, or padding, obstructing the knee. The surgeon removed so much damaged tissue that my knee joints rub bone-on-bone when I walk, when I twist, or when I put pressure through them.

My excuse is that I played too much sport when I was young, but this doesn't show the whole picture. More likely, it's my sedentary middle-aged lifestyle with too much food and booze and only sporadic bursts of activity over the last three decades.

I've done endless physio for my knees and it hasn't got me far. I still carry pain with every step. I'm reasonably careful with my diet, at least I think I am. I cycle a little and I play cricket and garden, but afterwards pain drills through me and the painkillers keep coming; I take at least four paracetamol a day. Two in the morning and two in the evening, like clockwork.

When it's worse, I'll pop down to the surgery in the village and swallow whatever I'm given. Deep down, I know this isn't sustainable. If I keep this going, my health is likely to set off a major time-bomb inside, and I'm pretty sure the dial is already tick-ticking.

Truth is, I don't have time to think about it. Right now, I'm busy writing my Eden Chronicles novels, or ferrying the kids about, or decorating a room, or mending the boiler. Life is in the way.

I feel a twinge in my hamstring playing our first game of cricket for Bures, our local village team. Afterwards, I can't shake the nagging tightness but after several beers at the Eight Bells public house, I really don't care. I'm sure it will be better for next week's game, but I wonder if I'm losing my sense of being fit and well, because I'm struggling to remember what it feels like.

* * *

David's video surprises me. It's not a sales videos per se, more a journey of how he constructed his pool. I have a suspicion he's gambling that if his idea of a 'natural' swimming pool takes off, he'll be in massive demand. So, the videos are more:

"This is how I did it and I'm going to show you how you can do it too. My experience comes with warts and all, which I'm now going to share with you. By the end you'll understand that I know precisely what I'm talking about."

And, oh my days, there are plenty of warts: I laugh when I see him bravely trying to install the pump system in his freezing, ice-crusted pond. And I wince when his enormous sandbag wall collapses and he looks close to tears. He takes it all on the chin, saying simply, "Oh well," as if he were half expecting it.

Two weeks later and I'm sitting opposite David beside his pond in Norfolk with a handful of others from around the world; three fit young men from Argentina, Canada, and Australia respectively, a landscape designer from France, a curious Yorkshireman and me from Essex. In the flesh, David is much bigger than I expected. He has a distinctly red nose, and a face which looks permanently sunburned. His hair is even thicker and greyer than in the video.

He leads us through his overgrown garden, where we find tubs and barrels with bubbling pumps and algae and strange looking plants. His pool is a simple rectangle, with a swimming area of about twelve metres by four metres. Surrounding the swimming area is a three-metre wide planted zone, which tapers up to the pond's edge. Blue and yellow irises decorate the sides and bubbling water gently froths in each corner. It looks utterly charming.

David explains the rationale behind his obsession. When his kids returned from their first swimming lesson at the local pool, they complained of rashes, eyesores, and inflammation of the skin. The amount of chlorine in the pool outraged him. Chlorine, he informs us, is mild bleach. I'm pretty shocked to hear this, but on reflection, it must take something powerful to knock out all the microbes of organic matter and particles of bacteria that exist naturally in water.

We sit in a tiny, square, wooden hut, raised on large round posts a metre above the pond. He begins his presentation with a small blackboard and a piece of chalk. He's not a natural teacher, and as I look around, the others are as perplexed as I am. It's a painful, nervous display. Then someone asks a question and, as if by magic, the atmosphere changes. David relaxes and begins, enthusiastically, to expand.

Before long, we're examining his air-blowers, gutter-pipes, homemade clips, sections of drainpipe, flow rate, water-plants, and we even learn how he built his jetty. By this stage, I'm so overwhelmed with information I can barely take it all in. We're absorbed, firing question after question. This is David's format. He takes us through his wilderness garden to show us his mini-pool, just four metres wide on each side and five-feet deep, which highlights that his bubble-pump concept works for any size of pool.

This air pump, or bubble pump idea, which keeps water moving around the plants, is so simple. It replicates a river, or a lake, where a constant, gentle flow helps the plants remove the dirty particles from the water, cleaning it. He shows us two barrels, which helped him reach this conclusion. One is filled with plants and has clear-looking water underneath, the other, without plants, contains stagnant water.

David educates us on the depths and diameters of the various pipes he uses and openly admits where he went wrong. I learn about phosphates, nitrates and nutrients, air blowers and air stones, pond liners and pond membranes. The list of things I need to know is growing exponentially. The day is a dizzying flash of all things you need to build a swimming pond and David's enthusiasm is contagious; he's a man on a mission.

At the end of the presentation, he invites us to swim. The South American doesn't hesitate, nor does the Canadian. They're in their late twenties and super-fit, so they dive in and whoop ecstatically. I feel awkward. I brought my costume, but I'm not quite ready to plunge in as, among these muscle-ripped young men, I feel absolutely huge.

At dusk, I'm the last to leave. I shake David's huge hand and comment that there's no way any of us will not build a pool. He grins back, knowing he's done a good job on us.

As I drive home, I can see the whole thing in my mind's eye. I have a pretty good idea what my pond will look like and even how to construct it. I even know where I'll deposit the spoil. As I leave Norfolk, I wonder if mine will turn out like the ones in South America, Canada, Yorkshire and France.

I smile like an adolescent receiving his first kiss, and turn up the music. It's a nineties classic, '*Can you dig it,*' by The Mock Turtles. I'm blown away. The pond-gods have clearly meant this to be!

I'm definitely going to do this. It's exactly the kind of

project that will make our new home 'ours'. And maybe this is my route back to decent health and fitness. All I have to do is persuade Charlotte that this method really can work. I'll tell her it's going to be far cheaper than building a tradition swimming pool, and far more beautiful. She'll have a garden she can be proud of.

If I get stuck, I've got David at the end of the phone and he's already conquered all the known problems of self-building a swimming pond.

So, what could possibly go wrong?

Digging and Planning

The following day, I discover a selection of long wooden beams and some old pergola timbers I'd brought down from Yorkshire. Charlotte was aghast when she found out I was taking them, but right now they are a blessing. These beams delineate the rectangular swimming zone and I use a couple of long, coiled up ropes to define the planting zone surrounding it.

I explain to the kids what the idea is, and they are fleetingly excited. When I tell them the pool won't have any heating, their enthusiasm drains away. It nearly puts me off. In my excitement, I'd forgotten about this detail. I tell myself that no matter how cold the pond gets, and even if nobody swims in it for three-hundred and fifty-eight days of the year, for those four boiling hot English days when the country collectively grinds to a halt and we pant like dogs, it will be magnificent.

I settle for a total length of about twenty-five metres, which includes two sections of the planted zone at either end. It looks ridiculously big. When I consult the family, one of my girls thinks it should be larger, another thinks smaller. They're not really helping. I also need space for the spoil and, as the garden backs onto open fields, I know that a large bank would give us additional privacy and shelter from the prevailing westerly wind.

Every day I potter up and move the posts and rope around. Sometimes I shuffle the edging to the right, then a fraction to the left. It's only when an old friend, Paddy, comes around that I realise how amateur I've been. I've done everything by eye and I haven't even measured the sides. Paddy, a skilled joiner, shows me how to create a right angle, something I was taught years ago but which my brain vaporised. When accurately measured (he forces me to buy a 30m tape-measure) my original outline was way too close to the top of the property. When Paddy leaves, the pond has shifted five metres towards the house and is now a neat oblong. It's a great relief as I've just booked Dave the Digger. He's coming round to see what I have in mind. Dave digs holes for fun.

Dave lives across a couple of fields, and his daughter babysits for us. He looks a bit like a pirate. His deeply set eyes twinkle and his face bears a network of expressive lines. He walks with a slight limp and, by the way he talks, I wonder if he's slightly deaf. I show him what I am looking for and I give him some sketchy plans. I think he gets it, but, just in case, I give him David's video to study.

A week ago, I hired a light-blue one-ton digger to remove some roots and brash by the ditch pond. This was a test to see whether I could dig the pond myself. Operating the digger took a little getting used to, but it is off-the-charts fun for entertainment. For three days Charlotte watched me from the kitchen window, as I created something akin to the trenches of the Somme extracting no roots at all. And then I turned the digger over.

When the hire driver laughed at my endeavours in front of a seriously unamused Charlotte, I knew this skill set lived in a galaxy a long way beyond my current orbit. She subsequently hired a 'skilled operative' to remove the roots, and he did so, to my astonishment, in an hour. I told Charlotte that his efficiency was down to my initial hard work. Furthermore, my digger didn't have the necessary ooomph for the root extractions.

She rolled her eyes. "If you're going to make this pond, find a professional to dig it."

I'm in complete agreement.

When Dave tells me he's got a two-tonne digger, my eyebrows lift, I've expected at least a five-tonner and when I talk to brother Ed, he's surprised too. I ask how long the dig will take. Dave reckons he can excavate the pond in two to three weeks, subject to the weather. I'm impressed.

He's busy for the next six weeks, so we'll see him in early July.

I can hardly wait.

While watching the opening batsmen flail the opposition bowling to all parts of Bures's delightfully pretty cricket ground, I try to explain the idea of a swimming pond, or swim-pond, to the ensemble in the pavilion. There's a lot of:

"Ooh, that sounds really interesting, James," which actually means, "I don't understand what you're talking about, but I'll pretend I do," stitched with "You're absolutely bonkers."

No-one gets why you need to add plants. The river Stour, the county line between Suffolk and Essex which runs directly alongside the ground, weaves a neat path through a grove of tall willows that frame the medieval square church tower. I describe what I mean by using the river as an example. It doesn't work. One person points out that it would save a lot of time and money if I just swam in the river like everyone else. It's a good point, but I tell them my pool will be different because it won't have any run off from fertilisers, or pesticides, or cattle dung leaching into it. This shuts them up.

Online, I search for coils of water pipe, sections of drainpipes, landscaping material, jubilee clips, air stones, and more accessories. I'm making it up as I go and as I thumb my notebook for reminders, I have moments of panic, not quite believing what I'm doing.

My parents come around to understand what my pond idea is about. They are the two most understanding and encouraging people in the world, and they always, always lend a supporting voice. After I've described how the pond will work, they are lost for words. Mum asks three times why I need plants. Dad asks if I need planning permission. I'm tempted to give them David's video, but Dave the Digger still has it. As for planning, this hasn't even crossed my mind. I shouldn't think so, I tell him. After all, the pond is miles from anyone and it's going to be a wildlife haven. This is the only part of the entire conversation which makes sense to him and he nods his head politely as if this is clearly a decent endeavour.

My parents have a classic blue-tiled pool, perfect for cooling off in, but it's not so great if you want to swim lengths. Dad, who is a strong, tall man, once did six lengths underwater, which we kids considered was the greatest sporting achievement of all time. Many years later, I realised this was basically six underwater push-offs.

They live two houses down our little lane and their house is an open house for us, which includes the pool. So why on earth, I can hear them say, would you want to build a murky pond? These chats are getting tricky, especially as no-one has ever heard of an organic pool, or swim-pond, or whatever they're called. Maybe my descriptive powers don't do the concept justice, or maybe they can tell that I don't really know what I'm doing.

Afterwards, Charlotte pulls me aside and asks me, in all seriousness, whether the whole thing is a good idea. I'm wondering if they're colluding against me.

"Charlotte, dear, can I have a brief word in your ear? About James."

I promise her that one day the pond will be spectacular. She gives me one of her looks, which says,

"You'd better be right, because you're getting in rather too deep to be mucking around."

Snap!

It's a warm July morning when Dave the Digger arrives. He's early because of the extended hot weather. Our bathroom window looks out over the lawn, the end of which will shortly have a vast hole in it. While brushing my teeth, I peer down in trepidation at this significant moment as Dave offloads his digger from his low-loader and disappears back home for his dumper truck.

The idea is that while he digs, I move the soil out of the way using the dumper. This might speed things up, but Dave is a solo operator with so much experience that I wonder if I'll get in his way.

For the rest of the morning, we re-examine the project area and outline exactly where the spoil (the dug-up soil) will go, and double-check the planting and swimming zone areas.

Dave finally jumps on his red Kubota digger and draws his bucket head along the ground in a series of reasonably neat lines that determine the left-hand edge of the swimming zone. It's the moment I've been waiting for, and I can hardly contain my excitement.

When Charlotte comes out to see how Dave is getting along, I don't think she can really believe it's happening either. For the first time ever, she's lost for words.

I'm soon engrossed. Dave operates the digger as if it's an extension of his body. He scoops through layers of tarmac and lumps of concrete, the machine shuddering as he attacks the harder ground and he hardly misses a beat.

There are relaxation videos where you can watch a fire burn, or see crops in a field grow, or look into a wood and just enjoy the trees and plants moving in the breeze. Dave's digger driving should be there. It's a study of skill and concentration and it captivates me. Therapists should give it a try.

By the end of this first day, Dave has extracted about a foot of the oblong-sized swimming zone and moved the spoil into two piles, one of which consists of rubble and a smaller one of topsoil. There is precision with which he's going about his task, and I'm beginning to see why he thinks he'll have this vast hole dug in just two weeks.

I'm playing cricket on an artificial surface with a bunch of friends a few miles away in Suffolk. The start of the dig has given me a fresh boost and the summer sunshine brightens and warms the spirit. Guy, the owner of the cricket pitch, wants to know how the plans for the pond are coming along. He seems genuinely intrigued by the concept, as he owns a small lake crammed with plants. He asks whether this would work as a swimming pond. I tell him I'd have to get in and check it out—if he doesn't mind.

I look at his kidney-shaped lake with envy. He might have a swimming lake right there without even knowing it. At tea,

I wade in and find that the deepest part rises to just above my knees. You could easily swim in it, I say, if you're a child. I can see the disappointment in his eyes. His pond is rammed thick with lily pads, and I make a mental note to remember to return to ask for some of these in due course.

Today, my knees are hurting. I cannot put any weight on them—there's no cushioning there—so when I go out to bat, I use someone (normally a younger player) to run my runs. The expression is that I have 'a runner' and his job is to speed up and down the twenty-two yards of the wicket, while I merely stand and face the bowling, trying to connect with the ball. This is the only way I can bat with any usefulness, but the number of times I get run out after a huge muddle between me, the runner and the batsman at the other end, is ridiculous.

On this pleasant afternoon, with the sun shining and the WAGS (wives and girlfriends) making small talk over glasses of rosé, I'm batting and seeing the ball well. I've raced into the twenties and smack one of their bowlers for a huge six, high into a magnificent eucalyptus tree.

The next bowler drops the ball short. On this springy surface, the ball rears up and as it approaches my chest, I rock back, and swing my bat across my body. I connect sweetly with the ball. There's a smack of leather upon willow and from the corner of my eye I see the ball speeding away. Immediately, there is another crack, like a gunshot. Before I know what's happening, I'm lying in a heap on the ground.

I'm completely confused.

The wicketkeeper asks if I clubbed my head on the follow-through. I stare at him in bewilderment. I'm pretty sure I'd be rubbing a throbbing head bruise by now. The players swarm around and it doesn't take long to figure out what happened. My ankle is numb, like the moment after a bee sting, when you can sense the venom in you, but you haven't yet felt the sting.

As I get up, I wonder if I've twisted my ankle, but I've done that before and it's instant agony. Besides, it doesn't explain the sound of the rifle-like crack. I limp off with two players supporting me and sit down. One of their bowlers (who I had clobbered into the eucalyptus) tells me it's what I deserve. It's meant in jest, but I struggle to find it funny.

One player's wife claims to have some medical knowledge. I tentatively remove my cricket boots and socks. She gives me a knowing look and, by the uneasy silence, it dawns on all the bystanders that this is more serious than a sprain.

Right now, if you feel your Achilles tendon (directly above your heel), it's hard, like a bone, with a bit of 'give'. Now, sitting by the cricket field, I push my finger into a gap the width of a single KitKat bar. In place of the hard, bone-like tendon, it feels soggy, like a soufflé. Her prognosis is that my Achilles has severed. I know she's right and it would explain the rifle crack just after I'd hit the ball. The same thing happened to her husband some years ago, she tells me, and she gives me a look and says, "you poor bastard."

The shock that dampened the pain is wearing off, and it's not long before a heavy throbbing begins as my nervous system re-registers. I gobble paracetamol as Charlotte turns up and drives the car over the outfield towards the pavilion.

Twenty minutes later and I'm sitting in a wheelchair outside A&E with tears rolling down my cheeks. It's happened again. Another injury, another failing body-part. Word has got around fast and from the few anecdotes I receive from a couple of friendly doctors and other friends, I realise this is going to take months to heal.

A&E goes in a blur. Before I know it, the Achilles specialist sets the bottom half of my leg in a neat lilac-blue cast. At home, I'm not sure what's happening, but I end up in the spare room. My head is swimming. The codeine has kicked in again.

I wake in the middle of the night with my ankle pulsating, and it's hard to get comfortable. I have an overriding thought. What on earth do I do with the pond?

We'll decide when I've spoken to Dave in the morning. Dave doesn't need managing, but the dig is just one part of the overall mix. There's a myriad of things to sort out: the protective membrane and plastic liner, tens of tons of sand and gravel, the retaining wall in the swimming area, the sand-and-cement bag wall, the overflow, air-circuits and air-pump system, let alone the plants.

The list is endless.

Either I battle on and muddle through, or I put the pond on hold. And if I put it on hold, chances are this dream of mine will never happen.

Above: The digger makes the first incision.

Dave, the digger. Legend.

Arriving at A&E.

The lilac cast

Below: Dave getting stuck in

The pond dig

Early days of the bund, which is rolled over extensively by the digger.

The base of the pond nears completion.

Dave's Dig, Boot and Wedges

My toes point downwards, permanently, like a ballerina en pointe. The plaster-cast-guy set the foot in this unnatural position because the severed tendons of the Achilles need to fuse. Attempting to put weight on my ankle is the biggest no-no of all, so it's double-crutches time. I'm good at crutches and there are several pairs stored in the loft.

Charlotte unearths a sporting-green pair from twenty-five years ago when I severed my anterior cruciate ligament in a freak disco accident in the Alps. On that occasion, I slipped on a pile of ice cubes and someone jumped on me. The top half of my leg went in one direction, everything else in the other. To rub salt in, a burly French bouncer picked me up and literally threw me out of the nightclub straight into a snowdrift. Later, a bunch of incredibly drunk friends dragged me, freezing cold by then, back to our chalet on a plastic bag. These French crutches are still more comfortable than the standard NHS offer.

When I hobble out to see Dave, he stares at me, one eye

bulging more than the other. He doesn't smoke, but part of his bottom lip sags where a roll-up should be.

'What in the hell have you done?' he exclaims, in a concerned way, his voice louder than usual.

I explain. Charlotte joins us, concerned that I've hobbled all the way to the dig while off my head on codeine. I think she's wondering what I'll say. It's like a weird committee meeting. His next question is the one I'd expected.

"Do you want me to continue? I haven't got far," he begins, pointing at the outline he's scraped off. "We can restart... when you're better." It's a kind gesture.

A snapped Achilles can take up to six months to get right with or without an operation. That leads us into winter. And the possibility of complications for someone in my shape and of my age is high.

"I think we should carry on," I reply.

Charlotte has advised caution, but we've talked it through. I reckon that by the time Dave has dug the pond, I'll be fitter and I remind her that this isn't a competition and I'm not in a great hurry. We have plenty of time. I think Charlotte understands what I'm attempting to do and she backs off from influencing the decision. I'm relieved and so is Dave, who smiles, slaps me on the shoulders and bounds back into the red cab of the Kubota.

Watching Dave restart the excavation is even more mesmerising through the lens of my powerful medication. It's the rhythm of his work, the precision of how the digger bucket eats into the ground at perfect, laser-accurate intervals, and how he makes every scoopful count. After half-an-hour, I notice Dave giving me a strange look and I speculate that he's wondering if I'm OK. Anyway, the deep throbbing pain has started again. I need to lie down.

I'm determined not to let this setback get to me. To keep myself busy, I buy a French and a German language course online with the strong intention of expanding my European linguistic skills. In theory, it's a wonderful idea, but the drugs send me to sleep, or I hallucinate, and I can't remember anything. I try writing, but after a couple of pages I re-read a pile of drivel. The words jump about like startled frogs.

Charlotte has remained calm, but I can sense the added burden I've put on her. It's all the driving depositing and collecting the kids, mowing the lawn, filling the biomass boiler with pellets, trimming the hedges, and the list goes on. My period of inaction won't last, I hope, but while this household friction lingers, I keep out of the way as much as possible.

Charlotte is rather like a classic old-school nurse. A couple of paracetamol, rest, and a large or small whisky—depending on the ailment—are her main panaceas. She has little sympathy unless, ironically, it's her. Then, she demands everyone's full attention. The children and I know this, so we're rarely sick and perhaps that's how it should be. After all, the human body has a remarkable capacity to sort stuff out if you let it get on with it.

By the end of the first week, Dave has carved a significant oblong-shaped hole out of the old farmyard. This will be the deeper swimming-zone in the middle. As a result, the spoil bund has grown exponentially. After several deposits of the dumper truck, he runs over the earth with the digger, pasting it into the ground. As the bund increases in size, it looks like a croissant quietly rising in a massive oven.

The incredible amount of rubble surprises even Dave. He digs up mangled metal, pipes, twisted wire and plastic cables, half-crushed bricks and concrete blocks, slabs of tarmac, a selection of cobbles and large shards of flint. As the pond shape forms, I'm concerned that the plastic membrane, or liner, might push onto sharp metal or flint edges. And the one thing I do not want is a punctured liner.

I try to work out ways of blanketing the ground, but every option comes with a hefty price tag. It's an extensive area to fill, and aggregates, like sand and gravel, are more expensive than I'd budgeted for.

Dave digs a ramp into the swimming zone and checks the depth. I think two metres will be about right. After all, the deeper it is, the colder the pond will be. And then I remember David's warning that nothing should run into the pond, so the perimeter of the pond must be higher than the surrounding area. Dave understands and tells me he'll use topsoil to bank up the edges. The pond height is a guessing game until his trusty laser-level comes out, but it turns out his accuracy from 'eye' is amazing.

There will be a retaining wall around the four sides of the swimming zone and I have a terrible feeling I never allowed for the bulk of the blocks. I explain this to Dave, who neatly trims off a section of soil as if it were butter. When the digger claw tucks into the last few inches on the bottom of the pool, the clay changes colour from light yellow to a curious speckled white. It is gooey and sticky and reminds me of thick nougat with chocolate speckles. It's a good thing the weather has held, as this stuff would be diabolical to move when wet.

* * *

I develop a new medical condition. The codeine has blocked me up so much that the idea of expelling anything becomes more problematic than my tender Achilles. I wasn't aware of this side-effect and after a few more days, my constipation is a major issue. I'm reluctant to involve Charlotte, as she has enough on her plate right now. I really don't want to give her another 'me' problem to deal with.

I sit on the loo straining. It's the only way I can budge what feels like a significant chunk of coal lodged in my passages. Eventually, when it finally pops out, blood accompanies and splashes around the porcelain. I have conceived volcanic rock wrapped in a bramble. It's miserable.

I ring my mother with a desperation in my voice she instantly recognises. She immediately brings over some herbal pills. She tells me she had a similar condition after we were born and gives me a big, sympathetic hug. It's a curious bonding moment and I realise just how incredibly brave she's been over the years. Mercifully, these pills do the trick.

Two weeks later and I'm booked in for an operation to sew my Achilles tendon back together. Charlotte drives me to the hospital and we end up in a small private room chatting with the nurses. I'm told to undress and slip into one of those flimsy hospital gowns where one's bottom gets a little airy. I'm nervous and Charlotte knows it. She makes unnatural consoling noises and tells me I'll be on the mend before I know it, but we both know this is going to be a long and difficult journey. And the op might not even work.

The anaesthetist arrives and does all the checks and tells me what to expect. A little while later, a couple of nurses appear to take me down to the operating theatre on their special trolley. They ask if I'm ready. I nod and glance nervously at Charlotte, as a young doctor I've never seen before enters the room examining my clipboard. As he scans my lengthy medical history, he explains how they'll cut off the cast in theatre and how they stitch the Achilles tendon back together again.

Then, something rather extraordinary happens.

He blurts out that my operation is a dangerous move. Not only am I too old, he says, scanning me, but I'm too unfit. I admit I'm not in the best physical shape, but I lie and tell him this is a temporary condition.

"An operation on the Achilles is really for those who will continue playing sport," he says, glancing at me, "at a higher level."

He's clearly never come across the mighty Bures cricket team before.

The doc examines my medical history again and murmurs something about my knees before nodding his head knowingly. He says that the chances of an operation being a success are low, because there's more chance of infection because of the lack of blood in the area. Besides, the operation itself is not a certainty, as the Achilles heel presents limited tissue to work with.

"And the alternative is...?" I respond, perplexed. I leave the question hanging.

"The alternative is to let nature take its course," he says. "The ankle can live in a boot with various heel-wedges to support it. Slowly and surely, so long as you don't bash it, the tendon knits together. As it strengthens, the heel moves to the ground by removing the wedges at intervals. It's a longer process, but safer," he tells me with a winning smile. "And just so you know, the result is absolutely identical. It's your choice. What do you want to do?"

I don't know what to think. I'm psyched up for having this operation and a quick word will see me wheeled towards the scalpel. But his argument is compelling. If I can avoid being cut up again, then I'm sure that would be a good thing.

Charlotte bursts out laughing and shrugs. "Your call," she says.

One minute I'm sitting in a hospital gown moments away from a knock-out series of drugs and going under the knife, the next I'm re-dressing, waving at the nurses and hobbling back to the car.

I have a slightly guilty feeling as though I've been told off for sneaking into a first-class train compartment by a ticket inspector. Then again, I think I might have dodged a bullet.

Retrospectively, I believe it was an excellent decision. That young surgeon who flashed into my life for just a few minutes and whose name I cannot remember made a pretty good call.

On the phone, my cousin informs me that his friend severed his Achilles not once, but twice before it knitted. He'd had to start afresh each time. "Absolute bloody nightmare," he tells me. It's not a reassuring conversation.

My foot remains in the lilac cast for another week. When I return to the hospital, the chirpy plaster-cast technician explains how I must keep my ankle perfectly still so he can slide it into a mammoth grey boot contraption, which looks like a ski boot made for Andre the giant.

Knowing that a tiny knock will send me slipping down

the snake all the way to the beginning fills me with dread. As my foot slips in I hold my breath. Every nudge is like an electric shock. My calf muscle is already pathetically weak and my ankle feels like it's being held together by a sliver of skin.

Inside the heel of the boot are five wedges, like cheeses. Each cheese is a centimetre tall, stacked up like an inner high-heel to support my en pointe foot. The wedge height is supposed to marry with the angle of my plaster-set ankle and every two weeks I have to remove one wedge.

As I stand and press down, the pain is excruciating. I can't breathe. But I'm told that by easing my weight onto my ankle in the next forty-eight hours, the tendon will 'find' its new level.

I wear this heavy boot day and night. Initially, it's agony, and I resort to prolonged spells in the arms of codeine. It's the acute angle of my foot that makes walking impossible, and Dave perfectly understands when I don't go out.

Besides my sore bum, my knees decide this is a suitable moment to join in the fun. I wonder if this recent deterioration is from arthritis. I know I have to put weight on the foot, so I push through the pain barrier and ever so slowly, movement gets easier. I'm struggling though and feeling particularly low, especially as I know I've got to do this whole wedge thing another four times.

And the first one, I'm told, is one of the easiest.

* * *

Dave scrapes back the area from the edge of the main swimming zone to the perimeter of the pond with incredible skill. Using his bucket, he tapers the earth until its banked sides look like a muddy velodrome. One day, aquatic-plants will grow here, and this reminds me to research where to find them.

By the end of the first week in my enormous boot, I'm more confident in pressing on the heel and the pain reduces. However, because of the blocking effects of codeine, every time I sit down I require the comfort of a rubber ring.

Then, as if the Gods of Pain haven't had enough, I wake up one morning with an excruciating toothache. With my tongue, I feel huge cavities in my molars, like valleys. Sharp pain flies along the nerve networks in my head with a constancy which is exhausting. It's like being permanently electrocuted.

All I need is a bash on the head and a kick in the groin for there to be barely any part of me free from pain. I wonder if anything else will decide to give up the ghost. I'm so wired with drugs and so stressed that I'm starting to think this pain is an expression of this trauma and toxicity.

Maybe my body is trying to tell me something, but I don't know how to listen to it.

A couple of days later and a young, recently qualified dentist from Chile repairs my ground-down teeth with a putty which sets instantly. It flicks off the pain like a switch. Then he takes a mould filled with even more putty and crams it onto my bottom jaw. He informs me I'm going to have to sleep with a rubber mouth guard for the rest of my days. I'm stunned.

'Is there no other way of dealing with this?' I ask.

He shakes his head, almost apologetically, and tells me to come back in a few days to make sure it fits.

* * *

Dave rings me and asks me to come up to the pond. He's hit on something in the corner, about a foot or so down. My imagination zooms into overdrive. I wonder if he's found a pile of Saxon coins, or a skeleton, or something of immense archaeological interest.

I don't know what I'm looking at when he shows me several foot-long round clay pipes. They're cream-coloured and look old. I ask if they're valuable, and my heart sinks when he tells me they are part of a land-drain, probably laid after the war.

Problem is, this land-drain would appear to snake from the adjoining field into the middle of the pond and thereon, I suspect, into the ditch-pond nearby. I take a while to understand what this means. Land-drains draw in surface water and deposit it in a ditch, so I convince myself that the lie of the land moves away from the pond to the other side of the field.

If I'm wrong and my eyes are deceiving me, all the water from the field will flow into my new pond. Oh dear. This could be a disaster. A high water-table isn't something I've considered until now, but I remember David mentioning it in his video. I take comfort that one day soon the pond will have a thick plastic liner filled with two hundred cubic metres of water on top, so I bury my initial concerns.

Dave removes the pipes just as the farmer turns up to see how it's all going. Chris has one of those eternally youthful faces helped by a mop of blond hair. It's hard to get a straight answer from him and his outlook on most things is more often than not met by a shrug, a murmur, and a smile.

He's as perplexed by the land drain as we are and since the hot weather has left everything bone dry, there's no way of knowing which way it heads. In any event, there are more pressing issues to deal with, like buying pond fleece and a liner.

And if and when a liner arrives, I'll have to find twenty to thirty people to shift what will be a colossally unwieldy item and somehow fold it into the corners.

With my legs in their current state, I won't be lifting a finger.

* * *

Dave returns on Monday morning with some exciting news. In the pub over the weekend, he chatted to a bloke who installs liners in reservoirs for tomato growers. He gives me Martin's number and I call him. Martin, or Marty, is an ex-marine and sounds like it, gruff and to the point. He's happy to come and look.

Marty tells me they have a special machine, which welds, or melts, each section into place after they've been cut and measured. Weather permitting, the lining will be complete in just a day or two. This is excellent news. I no longer have to bribe twenty friends with beer and burgers.

Dave's digger makes a smooth finish all the way round, but there's no hiding the sharp edges of flint and metal that still protrude. I still can't stop thinking how a shard of metal will, under the immense weight of the water, pierce the liner. It's a thought I can't dislodge from my brain. Eventually I wake up in the middle of the night worrying about a leak. This is doubly annoying, as sleep right now is not assisted by the invasive rubbery mouthguard I'm trying to get used to.

An online search pushes me towards reconditioned sand, which is the fine grit and rubber that comes out of road sweepers. It's cheap, and I order forty tonnes. Dave spoons this curious pewter-coloured mix into piles and, feeling more comfortable and active in Andre's boot, I rake this strange, soft, dark medium evenly around the surface. It's so liberating to be physically involved.

Dave's final work for now is to bank up the sides with the topsoil he saved when pulling back the initial soil. He checks his laser level before rolling endlessly up and down the banks, firming it in and leaving a raised, hardened finish.

The pond dig is now complete. It looks like a huge round eye with a rectangular retina. The croissant-like bund is now cooked and shields the view across the field.

As we move towards the end of September, with the weather remaining fine, Paul and Ron, two bricklayers who've been patching up the house, set about building the retaining wall on the inside of the swimming zone.

Pills and Pop!

I stare at my pile of pharmaceutical pills that sit in their machined, regimented, foil jackets that take up an entire shelf of our bathroom cabinet. How did I get so many so quickly?

It strikes me I'm following a path trodden by my mother and before her, her mother. Both rely, or in Granny's case, relied, on pills prescribed by the local GP.

Mum, for pain management over the last five decades following a terrible back injury. She needs her prescription drugs. I know she absolutely wishes she didn't, and has tried to come off them, but there was always something else, another problem, another operation.

Granny had a dispensing cabinet, which she laboriously filled every week. I remember how she had one drug for one ailment, another two for further problems, a smaller pill for the thing that the first drug didn't quite do and larger ones for something the second one did too much of. Then there was one more to compensate for the side-effect of the second, or the third, or the fourth pill. And on it went.

My mother bemoaned the number of pills Granny chuffed in the last years of her life. They may have kept her alive, but I suspect these pills ganged up into a toxic stew inside her and leached poison into her body and her brain. And when she tried to wean herself off the drugs, she just couldn't. Her dependency made it impossible. Her final years were a grim, dementia-filled mess that decimated the lives around her, particularly mother's.

Ironically, now it's mum's turn. And when I look at my collection, I wonder if this is a family trait where I'm catching up fast.

Over the last fifty years, there's barely a square inch of my mother that hasn't been operated on, toyed with, or, should I say, doctored. It's hard for Mum to have followed any other route as both her father and her brother, Kiff, were highly regarded, compassionate doctors with a wonderful bedside manner and tons of common sense. It goes without saying that they practice the medicine they were taught, which relies almost exclusively on pharmaceuticals.

Right now, when my teeth, tummy, bum, knees and ankle are screaming at me, I, too, run to the pill shelf. Thing is, I know these work like band-aids but don't address the real problem of why my body is in such a mess. Deep down, I know I must do something different, and I suspect this nightmare only stops when I take full responsibility for what goes into me.

The question is, how on earth am I going to do that?

I blindly search the internet for ways of making myself better, but inwardly I know there's no quick fix, no miracle diet, no unique superfood, no magic pill, as any of thousands of sites on the internet might claim.

I sense that what I'm after is a prescription for life.

The more certain I am of this approach, the more I keep coming up against a barrier of uncertainty, a kind of fear, which urges me not to sever the umbilical cord of medical, or rather, pharmaceutical dependency. In the back of my mind, a voice tells me to keep taking the drugs, or suffer more.

I am beginning to think I've outsourced my health to a bunch of people who aren't interested in me and it has spun out of control. I make a vow that somehow I'm going to find a way out of this mess.

* * *

Paul and Ron are in their thirties, with middle-of-a-rugby-scrum physiques and arms as thick as my thighs. There's an easy way about them and they're happy to chat and drink tea; white with five.

In no time, they excavate the wall's foundation and quickly batten the edges with boards. On cue, a cement mixer sneaks up the old roadway that leads to the pond. The driver offers a thick hose to Paul, who fills up the space between the boards with gloopy cement. Both Ron and Paul chop the 'muck' by repeatedly banging a large 2x4 section of wood over the top to release air bubbles trapped in the mixture. They're done in a couple of hours, and now we wait for the foundations to set.

The late summer sun beams down, and the temperature is a blissful blend of never too hot or too cold. A week later, and the concrete is hard enough to build on. Using a wide board as a chute, they slide grey breeze blocks into the pool area and stack them neatly into piles. Soon, the first three courses line the pool. Paul cements the blocks, while Ron controls the concrete mix at a satisfyingly relentless rate.

Their speed and accuracy is deeply impressive and while I had imagined myself doing this work when David was taking us through the build process, I'm relieved; the wall is razor straight, and plum level. My effort would look nothing like this, and no, I'm not being hard on myself.

Two days later, and from our bathroom window, I look down upon a perfect oblong box which measures 18 metres long by five wide and is approximately one and a half metres high. On three sides, the top of the wall adjoins a level, flat area, where a singular paving slab will run all the way round, creating a ledge, but it reminds me I haven't sourced any paving.

From this neat block-box in the pond, the sides graduate up to the outer-edge of the pool. The entire structure looks enormous.

I may be sore all over, but I'm absolutely fizzing with excitement. I can't stop smiling as I try to imagine how it will look filled; fresh water, buzzing dragonflies, plants filling the sides, swimmers and swallows.

This burst of joy is timely. I'm about to remove boot wedge number one. The second most painful cheese of them all.

That night in bed, I'm woken by a tremendous rumble of thunder. The noise of the storm builds until Charlotte scampers around the house, closing the windows. Summer's fiery streak has broken. I hear rain washing the roof tiles until I fall asleep.

At dawn, it's hard to believe the view from our bathroom window. A huge puddle, or pond, covers most of the lawn at the back of the house. Three ducks are swimming on it and fly off noisily as I hobble up to the pond on my crutches. My heart beats like crazy in nervous anticipation of what I might find.

I stare in, but I'm not sure what I'm looking at; I can see a few of inches of water inside... and slowly my eyes assimilate that sections of grey blocks lie in the pond, toppled over. It's the same story on both sides.

It doesn't take long to work out that the clay Dave pushed behind has expanded and popped the wall, as if someone has blown it up. I let out a nervous laugh and try not to burst into tears. Then I hobble numbly around the pond a few times. Dave turns up and stares at it, about as dumbfounded as me, apologising and shaking his head in disbelief.

Right now, I feel altogether helpless and bruised all over.

* * *

Fortunately, there's a lad called Jason who's working on our house (Paul and Ron have moved to another job) who says he'll patch it up over the weekend. I borrow the neighbour's pump to draw out the water and Jason insists I hire four Acrows to prop up the wall. These are large, adjustable metal poles with square ends which extend and retract via a screw mechanism.

Jason is all wire and muscle. He has a long, handsome face, and short, cropped, jet black hair. All over him are large tattoos, one of which declares, from within a bouquet of roses, his eternal love for his mother. He approaches his work as if the special forces have trained him. But there's a charm and an easygoing air and his warm, broad smile underlies his discipline. He works relentlessly, single-handedly rebuilding the wall, propping up his work with the Acrows pushed against scaffold boards to prevent another collapse. His energy makes me feel rather puny.

Afterwards, we have a beer and a smoke. Jason smokes his roll-up slowly and easily compared to me. He has a languid way and uses neat expressions with smiley mannerisms. He wants to start his own company, and although there's little doubt he'll produce amazing work, I wonder if he's more of an artist at heart. Jason's a man who delights in his work.

I buy another truck load of shingle and Dave places it neatly behind Jason's new wall. The wall is steady and strong and even though Jason insists the wall won't pop again, I'm reluctant to remove the supports.

It's now late October and the lovely Indian summer is over. The smell of seasonal change fills the air and increasingly frosty nights leave a white dusting on the lawn. A fleecy membrane arrives in three giant rolls and I'm immediately heartened by the cushioning—it's way thicker than I'd expected. We roll it out over the banks and stretch it to fit. In the late autumn sunshine, its whiteness is blinding. It looks like fresh winter snow.

As we head into November, the temperature drops below zero, and in some areas there's a dusting of snow. I tell the children to grab a jacket, scarf and woolly hat. We pretend it's been snowing and pose, careful not to get the muddy edges into camera shot. We take a couple of selfies and load the best ones onto Facebook.

Our lovely new neighbour fires back a comment that she can't believe we've had so much snow; none where they are.

The kids think this is hilarious, but there's a lesson there. Sometimes you have to check things for yourself and not rely on 'trusted' sources. I doubt they'll get it.

* * *

After I'm faking snow pictures, I watch a video of an eccentric called Wim Hof, otherwise known as The Ice Man, plunge into freezing waters as though it is perfectly normal. Wim, a gnarly, bearded Dutchman, holds a bunch of world records for physical acts in freezing temperatures and, as I quickly learn, has a trophy room filled with implausible physical feats, like running up Mount Everest in a pair of shorts.

I'm drawn to this madness and discover Wim's process is, simply, deep repetitive breathing and breath-holds, followed by exposure to the cold.

I'm not sure I completely understand what it's supposed to do (something about controlling the autonomous nervous system—whatever that is) but I dig around and watch more videos which explain his breathing method. And I read a bunch of glowing testimonials of people who swear by this lunacy.

Wim sees the cold as nature's educator; a professor of rediscovering one's power. It's a big claim. I look at the pond and wonder whether I will ever swim in its freezing winter water. I shake my head. Right now, it seems unlikely I'll ever swim in it at all.

Right: My huge "Andre the Giant" ski boot with its five wedges

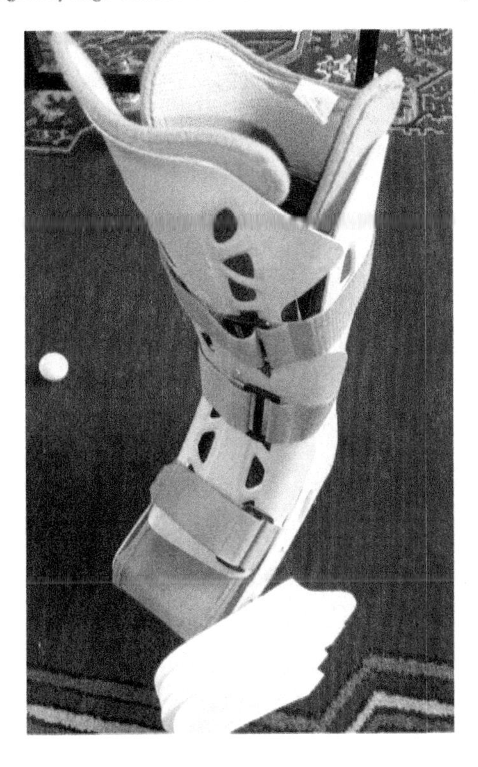

With the swimming area dug, Dave pulls back the sides for the planting area

The retaining block wall before, and after the storm which decimated the area. Dave looks on in shock.

Above: A thick white lining above the black sand as added protection.
Below: The kids and I play in the... snow! Note the plastic bag on my leg.

Wim's methods don't cost a thing. After all, breathing is free, as is immersing oneself in cold water. I download the Wim Hof Method app on my phone, wondering if I've missed some crucial and possibly more complicated element.

The app has a circular breathing guide, which expands and contracts as one breathes, while Wim's grainy, yet soothing voice tells me what to do.

I lie down, relax, and try it. To my immense surprise, after completing three rounds of thirty breaths with a breath-hold after each round, I'm high—in an easy, joyous way—in total contrast to the woozy, out-of-control blur of codeine.

I don't know if this is the way ahead. It's whacky and I really don't want to go into cold water. I look into it further and learn that the idea of his breathing method is a shortcut to reaching a deep meditative state. While I've heard about meditation, I know little about it, or why it's so important, but apparently this is a big thing.

Even though I've had a curious and uplifting experience, I continue my quest for another kind of inspiration, perhaps something more routine. Thing is, because I'm so used to our patch-it-up culture, I know I'm searching for a quick fix, and deep down I understand that this isn't available.

One day, I tell myself, when I'm out of Andre's boot, I'll re-start my bicycling and get super-fit. I've convinced myself that my problems stem from a lack of fitness. What I fail to notice is that I'm not mentally fit either.

The more I concern myself with my conundrum, the greater I notice a feeling within, a voice perhaps, which is trying to get through, but which I keep ignoring.

I wonder if it's because I can't bear to hear what it has to say.

With the pond membrane now secured, I take delivery of the first of many 20 tonne-loads of sharp sand. Almost immediately, I get a call from Marty, the liner guy Digger Dave met in the pub. They can come this week. I'm elated; this is really happening. There's a long way to go, but lining the pond feels like it might be a turning point.

In the excitement of getting ready, I'm moving more than I have for months, so when I feel my ankle throbbing, I'm praying I haven't overdone things. Due to muscle wastage, my leg has shrivelled so much that Andre's boot simply drops off when I untie the straps. My legs are now a kind of Laurel and Hardy combination. The rest of me is round in comparison and I look like a cartoon caricature of myself.

A stubborn, throbbing ache in my heel has been building for a few days, as if my heel pad is permanently pressing hard onto a small pebble, bruising the bone underneath. Trying to examine my heels with knackered knees is nigh on impossible and as it's a chore to take off the boot (this is when the ankle is at its most vulnerable), I've put off removing it until I can't bear the smell, or the itchiness any more.

When Charlotte pulls off my sock, she wretches and leaves the room. This leaves me feeling nervous. She takes a picture and shows me. The underside of the heel is bright yellow, almost luminous, as if it's rotting. Yup, another visit to the local surgery, yet another prescription.

I'm intrigued by the hideousness of my foot and post the image on Instagram. The image shoots off to my middle daughter's phone and within ten minutes she runs in demanding I remove the offending image.

'You only put nice things on Instagram,' she tells me. "And *that* thing (my heel) is completely disgusting."

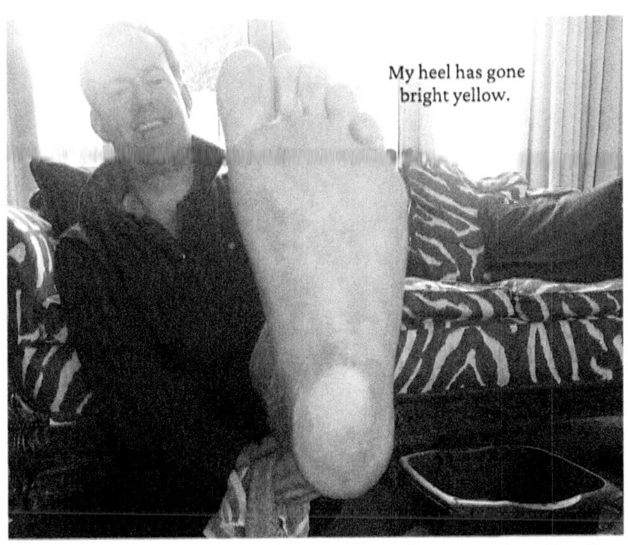

My heel has gone bright yellow.

The rebuilt wall with Acros placed across the pool. Pewter-coloured road-sand blankets the flint and rocky surface, which gives the liner an extra barrier.

Pain and Patio

Since the yellow-heel episode, I keep the ankle out of the boot as much as possible and use fresh air, sunlight and salt baths; I'll do anything to avoid visiting the doctor. When I do, they examine me, slap a print-out into my hand, which they know I'll never read, and wave me off with a fresh bag of expensive drugs. And now, when I look at them piled up on the bathroom cabinet, I can't remember what some of them are for.

In the back of my mind, all I can see is my grandmother's "tablet organiser" and call me paranoid, but every trip to the doctor reaffirms that I'm heading straight down the same narcotic-fuelled path.

I spend more and more time worrying about how I can get myself together, but I don't make any genuine progress. It's as if I'm trying to rediscover a fundamental piece of my human jigsaw, which I sense is probably staring me in the face. At every step, it feels as if there's a barrier I must push out of the way.

Somehow, I know I must find the courage to break my

dependence on these pills. The frustrating thing is that I know this can only come from within, and heading into uncharted territory with my health terrifies me. Then again, can it really get any worse?

* * *

Marty, the pond liner installer, has clipped blond hair and eyes that mourn the camaraderie of the services. He tells me his girlfriend is desperate for him to settle down to a desk job as he's always away lining reservoirs for supermarket suppliers.

One of his companions is older, has a broader build and is thinning on top, and I suspect he's the brains of the operation. The third member of their team, in a matching grey gym kit, literally jumps whenever Marty opens his mouth.

A long, fat roll of black plastic arrives on a trailer which looks as if it's about to collapse under the weight. I feel weak, and a little sick about how this singular roll will fill the sides of the pool.

When I ask how they're going to fold it into the swimming zone, they laugh and give me a look as if I'm a genuine half-wit. I've forgotten about their special machine, which heat-welds the plastic together. It turns out I could have had any pool-shape I wanted.

I've been grateful for the metal Acrows in case of another monsoon, but as they lift them out, I hold my breath hoping I won't have a repeat of the blown wall. This time, secured by tonnes of gravel behind them, the walls feel like those at Windsor Castle.

Before long, the three lads blanket the lawn with the black plastic and rush round, measuring and cutting with a knife which looks like a mega Stanley knife with terrifying superpowers. The thickness of the plastic is 1mm all over, and the welds, Marty explains, are far stronger than just folding it. I'm hoping he's right.

"Do they ever come apart?" I ask.

"Oh, occasionally," he replies casually.

I'm not overly reassured, but I sense he's playing with me. They cut and weld through a persistent drizzle and there's little I can do to help. The weather has turned with an intermittent mixture of heavy rain, gales and freezing sunny spells.

In no time, the lads have covered the block walls and the floor of the swimming zone shines in its new shiny, dark suit. As dusk arrives, they start on the sides of the wider planting zone before heading home. I spend some time staring at the black, gloss-like sheets in the dank rain, trying to imagine what it will look like filled with water and covered in plants. It's incredibly difficult.

Later, I decide to have a go at the Wim Hof breathing again. I follow the simple rhythmic pattern while lying on my back. After thirty deep breaths, I hold out the air after my exhale for as long as I can, which is barely a minute. I repeat this process for three rounds and, when I'm done, I hit a euphoric state again. My head is pleasantly buzzing. My body tingles as if I'd given it a rocket of adrenaline and I experience an emotional rush that has tears flowing down my cheeks. I don't even know why.

I'm blown away by how a simple thing like breathing can have such a profound effect. It sends me into a trance-like sensation where my mind empties.

Is this the meditative state I've heard so much about? Have I touched a part of myself I had neglected? My spirit, perhaps?

* * *

Marty appears bang on time the following morning and continues where he left off. I smell beer on his breath and wonder if he had a few with Dave in the Lamarsh Lion. There's only one more sheet to cut and weld, and this will sit below what will be the planting zone on the right.

I suddenly hear a terrible curse from Marty. When I reach him, blood is pumping out of a deep gash across his index finger into his palm. He's lacerated himself with the bionic Stanley knife.

Although he compresses his finger/palm with a cloth, blood has saturated the white rag and it looks like a scrunched up Japanese flag. I wonder if he's going to lose his finger, or bleed to death, so I suggest an ambulance. He gives me a wilting look. From the way he holds the digit above his head, it is a nasty cut, and although he tries not to show too much concern, I suspect it goes to the bone. I offer to drive him to hospital but he's rung his girlfriend, who appears ten minutes later, prickling, but calm, and whisks him away.

"It'll be quicker this way," he assures me, and I wonder if it isn't the first time he's had an accident like this. The other lads decide it's time to go home too.

I stare at the pond, a big black hole with one section missing. Charlotte has missed all the action and when I tell her, she shakes her head as if this is absolutely typical and somehow my fault.

This project is wearing thin with everybody.

When Marty reappears a few days later, his hand is in a bandage the size of one of those foamy-pointy hands you see at festivals. He says he's going to finish up and the other two are on their way.

I'm incredibly grateful he's back, and looking at his hand, I ask him if he's OK to continue. He squints at me as if I'm some kind of ninny, grins and soldiers on until the bandage is burgundy. After the final plastic sheet is welded into place and there's a fresh bandage around his hand, his mates roll out the white protective fabric. Then Dave arrives with his digger and dumper combination and places mounds of gravel and sand at neat intervals to hold it all down.

Marty is nearly done, but as the rain gets heavier, he tells me we have a big problem. I can't bear it and wonder if he's joking. He shakes his head and leads me to the side of the pond where we look over the fresh black liner. What concerns him is that the water underneath is pushing up against the moulded plastic liner. I can see what he means. The liner is already rising and it looks like air trapped underneath.

He checks the forecast on his phone with his good hand. It's for rain, mostly heavy. I can hear the worry in his voice.

"If the water table continues to rise, and it is," he says, "it's gonna bust the liner. Too much pressure going the wrong way."

Then I remember the water-table conversation with Dave and farmer Chris when we removed the clay land-drain pipes in the heat of summer.

He wonders whether I have enough sand and cement to weigh down the corners.

Almost immediately, I'm making cement as fast as I can. When the "muck" is ready, his mate pours the cement from a wheelbarrow into the corners. This crude method works. But the outline of a bubble develops in the middle of the pond. Marty notices it too.

He smiles and asks if there's anything else I've got.

"Like what?" I say.

"Like...any old paving slabs kicking about?"

"I haven't," I reply. "The only slabs we've got are on the patio."

He gives me a cheeky grin. "Are you thinking of getting a new patio soon?"

"One day," I reply, not registering what he means.

His eyes narrow. "That day might be closer than you think," he says, and he waits until I get it.

"You're bloody joking," I say. "You want me to lift the patio and slap it in the pond?"

"Sure," he says, as if this happens every day.

"The wife will kill me," I reply. "She already thinks this is the most stupid idea in the entire world."

He shrugs.

"What if I don't?" I ask.

"Listen," he says. "The pond will take four days to fill. By then, the water table will be too high and the pressure will split the liner."

"You sure?"

"You want to risk it?"

This is a nightmare. I don't, I really, really don't want to tear the liner at the very first hurdle, but I also don't want to lift our entire patio.

I'd better run this past Charlotte, so I ring her. Our conversation goes something like this.

Charlotte: "Why does my entire patio have to be sacrificed... for a bloody pond no one is ever going to swim in?"

"Otherwise," I struggle back, "we'll have to get a new liner and wait till the pond dries out to replace it. It could take months and it'll be incredibly expensive."

"Well, a new patio is several thousands of pounds," she

screams back. "And when are you going to have the time to build a new one?"

She says it in such a way that suggests my physical condition isn't even close to doing anything of the sort. And she's right.

"It's our one and only patio, darling,' she concludes, calmly. 'It's the one area we actually sit on."

"But there's nothing else," I plead. "It's an emergency."

I wonder if she thinks I'm playing a practical joke, especially with Marty and Dave snickering in the background.

Charlotte leaves it up to me, so I decide to go ahead. I tell myself the paving is an ugly collection of cheap, yellow riven concrete slabs, but I'm in a stupor of disbelief.

Dave's dumper truck is the only sensible way to move this volume so by the time we've uplifted and offloaded the slabs by the pond, not only is there an ugly, muddy, grey concrete area by the house, but the lawn has been destroyed. Everywhere I look, there is carnage.

I add "new patio," and "new lawn" to my lengthening to-do list. This unexpected episode has decimated my budget for pond plants. When I'm better, I tell myself, building a patio will be an excellent way of getting fitter and stronger. Right now, that feels miles off.

When Charlotte arrives home and sees the remains of the patio, she tells me the whole pond thing is a colossal white elephant and, frankly, a damn weird way of convalescing. When she's calmed down, she nods knowingly and remarks that she rather likes the Maltese cross effect the paving has achieved in the pond. It's a baffling response, but I can see she's trying hard to spin something positive.

I'm worried the paving will damage the liner, but Marty isn't.

"Hard to puncture," he says, "much easier to rip."

Marty's hand has bled through the puffy bandage again, and I'm hardly surprised after the shift he's put in. I offer him a beer, but he declines because of his antibiotics. He leaves me all the residual plastic and goes on his way.

Dave told me after this that Marty ended up behind a desk in the insurance world. It looks like his wife got her way after all.

Above: the huge liner is finally in place

Paving slabs hold the liner from water 'bubbling up' due to the high water table.

Pumps and Pipes

It's six weeks later and the rains have only just abated, so my decision to toss the patio in the pond was vindicated. It wasn't a popular choice though, and I am reminded daily of the appalling eyesore I created.

I'm now on the last heel-wedge of my giant boot, which I cover with a plastic bag tied with string to exclude water and mud. On the second-to-last wedge removal, the pain felt as if the ankle was being massaged by an angle-grinder but between wedge-removal-weeks, I'm walking around normally, if a little clumsily, and it is wonderful to be out and physically active.

Every ex-Achilles snapper I've talked to tells me that this final wedge is the worst, followed by weeks of physio and learning to walk again. This moment is coming up fast and I'm aware I need to get on with the sandbag wall and assemble David's curious and perplexing bubble-pump aeration system.

I fill hessian bags with a sand and cement mixture and place them on the wall above the block paving. It's a technique David dreamt up so the sand and gravel around the planting zone doesn't slip into the swimming area. I've embraced the idea because the bags are flexible enough for the air pipes to go through and will fit together in neat, organic-looking blobs, one on top of the other, like fat sausages. I'm aiming to lay three courses of these sand and cement bags all the way around.

With the cement mixer rolling, I make a dry, weak mix, as I don't want too much concrete contaminating the pool. I shovel this into a strange holding device I've copied off the internet. This odd-looking contraption has four equal lengths of wide, plastic pipe held in a frame, and I place hessian bags over the top of each one before manually filling them up. It doesn't always work and before long I have great sympathy for soldiers who assemble sandbag barriers in a flood-zone.

After the first thirty-two bags, I'm frazzled—and I haven't even reached the halfway mark on the first layer. Worryingly, I'm once again eating through my sand and cement reserves.

Mid-way through the second thirty-two and I'm hurting all over. My ankle throbs. Then, when I've completed the first circuit, Charlotte comes out, sees me limping, and tells me I'm being incredibly irresponsible. She's got a point.

I ring a friend named Gary and plead with him to come and help me out. Gary has wispy blond hair, large blue-eyes and apple-red cheeks. He's middle-aged, but if he didn't have such a big belly, he'd look about twenty-five. He's always smiling and cracking jokes. Gary brings Tom, a young, quiet, wiry fellow. He's a man of few words who wouldn't be out-of-place chewing a long strand of grass. He wears skinny jeans and an enormous pair of Doc Marten boots, so it looks as if he's about to trip up at any moment.

Gary helped me out while I temporarily ran the local cub-scout pack. I'd stepped in for a couple of months to keep the cub-pack going and stayed for a couple of years trying to recapture my youth while recalling what I'd loved about Scouting. It turns out this was fire, using knives, making camps in the woods, cooking, and outdoor games. So that is precisely what we did, and in spades. I loved it, the kids loved it and Gary enjoyed the fun and craziness as much as anyone.

These two are a good team and there's always a laugh and a joke pointed in my direction. After a simple explanation, it's clear I don't need to tell them what to do.

As I ice my swollen foot, I'm relieved they've taken over. Tom works like a robot and starts filling the sandbags at least three times faster than I could. While they get on with filling countless sandbags, I turn my full attention to David's aeration system, which I need to slot through the sides of the sandbag wall.

Understanding how all the tubes and drainpipes fit together has given me sleepless nights. In theory, it's simple: an air circuit, using a 20mm water pipe, runs around the perimeter of the swimming zone. On the four 'corners' of the circuit, I add in a T joint. On the spare end of each T, I add a shorter section of 20mm pipe that goes into the pond with a stopper in its end. Near this stopper, I drill a hole and push in a clear, 5mm pipe. On the other end of this clear pipe, I attach an air-stone which I suspend down a five-foot high, open-ended 68mm drainpipe. This drainpipe sits within a fatter, sealed drainpipe. All clear so far?

From each corner of the swimming zone, I lay out seven metres of perforated land-drain which expands across one quarter of the planted area. On one side, I keep the land-drains straight, on the other, for curiosities' sake, I bend the plastic so it snakes up and down. Next, I push one end of the land drain through the sandbag wall and into a standard T-bend drainage socket. I seal the other end of the land drain with plastic bags and wrap an incredible amount of duct tape around it.

At the Plumb Centre in town, I try to explain how it works, and the guy's eyebrows hyper-extend. I show him some of my diagrams and he diplomatically says he's never heard of anything like it. However, his colleague takes an interest and together we find an assortment of pipes, couplings, and fittings. When I hit the checkout, there is an extraordinary mixture of plastic pipes and strange connectors. The guy genuinely wishes me luck.

Back beside my pond, I set out the piping as described above. It takes a while to get the hang of how it pieces together, but soon I'm away. The blue 20mm pipe wraps neatly around the swimming zone like a ribbon around a parcel, and in each corner, I fit the bubble pumps to the T section I've pushed through the sandbag wall.

When I get to the part where I attach the 5mm clear tube, I attempt to wrestle an air stone to the other end but it simply will not go on. After an hour, I have a brainwave and dunk the end of the plastic pipe into boiling hot water, so it softens and expands. This works like a treat. Soon, each of my bubble pump contraptions is hooked up. They sit about five-feet into the pool and I place some paving around them for easy access later on if I need to change the air-stones, or make a repair. I lower the drainpipe pumps into the pond and slot them into the large hole of the T section, which connects to the land drains. All that remains is to turn the air blower on and hope for the best.

The entire method may sound complex, but in reality, it

isn't. David went to great lengths to explain why a 68mm drainpipe lowered to a certain depth in the pond is the optimal method of pulling water through the system. This was after trailing drainpipe prototypes with varying thicknesses. A 68mm drainpipe will fill a large bucket in seconds and David estimated that this simple method regenerates his pond every ten hours—which is amazing—if it's true.

I buy a simple 60 watt air blower online. This pushes air through the 20mm pipe circuit down into the air-stone which, via its bubbles, moves water from the land drains underneath the sand and gravel in the planted zone and into the main swimming zone.

If you're glossing over at these details, just think of it as a giant aquarium, but without fish. Or perhaps, more physics-minded folk will understand it as a reverse Venturi effect.

When I try to explain this method to anyone who is curious enough to ask, without exception they give me a look as if to say, "Do you actually, *seriously,* think this is going to work?"

A very basic couple of diagrams that shows, roughly, the pipe and pond schematic.

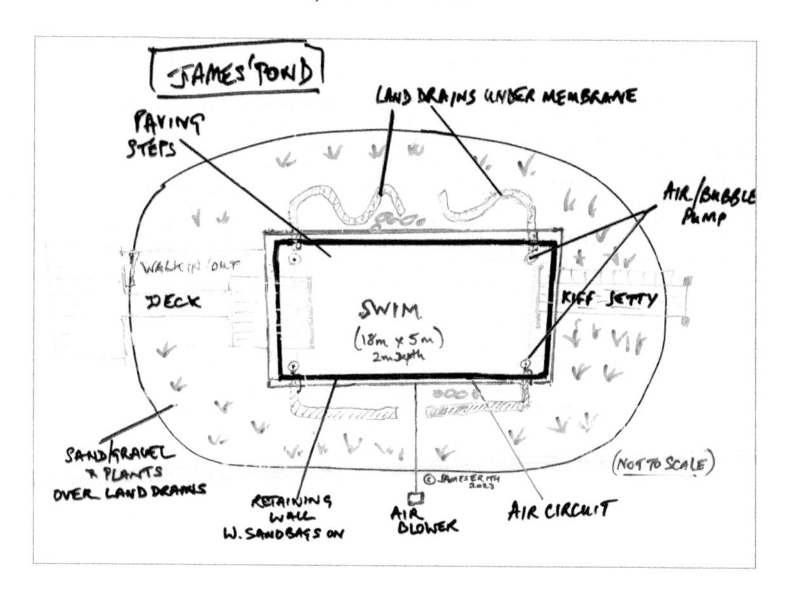

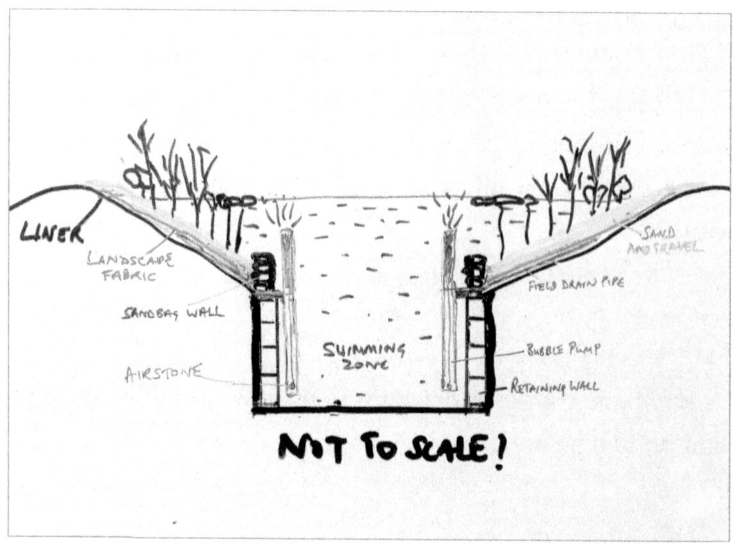

* * *

Digger Dave returns and scoops more sand from another fresh delivery into the dumper and disperses it around the planted zone. The sand disappears in a flash. When I look at these shallow mounds dotted over the planting area, it doesn't look like nearly enough. I'm hoping the 20 tons of gravel will bulk it up, but when this arrives, it blankets a thin section around the pool. I have massively underestimated the volume of aggregates and I figure I'll need approximately 100 tonnes. Now I understand why David added clay spoil back to his pond. Aggregates are expensive.

David admitted that in so doing, he'd added unwanted phosphates and nitrates to his pool and the effect was irreversible. The biology demands that if you strangle the plant's supply of nutrients at the roots, the plant must extract nutrients from the moving water in order to survive. This is how the water remains clear.

The water level is halfway up the sides of the swimming zone. I wonder how long it will take to fill naturally with our limited East Anglian rain. It's fortunate we're on a bore-hole rather than a water meter when we come to filling it up.

Gary and Tom complete the sandbag wall and the pond looks like a deconstructed military bunker with an envelope of water surrounded by sand and gravel. I nip down to the garden centre and buy one Arum Lily, which I ceremoniously plant. It looks like a tiny palm tree in a desert.

I turn my attention to the bund, or bank of spoil, and plant out one-hundred rooted plugs of catmint, variety; *Nepeta Six Hills Giant*. I don't know what will grow on this pile of clay, stone, metal and tarmac, but if the catmint takes, it should look spectacular over the summer months; a sea of purple flowers filled with busy bumble bees and dopey cats. If it doesn't... well, I haven't thought of an alternative.

* * *

It's time for my final boot-wedge to come out at the surgery. My Achilles has knitted together well, I'm told. I return home bootless and my first act is to deposit Andre's ski boot directly into the rubbish bin. For the first time in months my leg feels free, like a bird out of a cage, and I savour having air circulating around it once more.

My second is to ramp up on painkillers and I kick off the first of many exhausting and painful sessions of physiotherapy. My left leg muscles are vanishingly thin. By comparison, my right leg looks like a weightlifter's.

Unexpectedly, I now have to learn to walk again, which isn't as easy as you might think, especially on my dodgy knees.

Come March, the pool has filled with rainwater to the top of the swimming zone. I do the Wim Hof Method breathing every day, using the guide on my phone app. After the final exhale, I now get beyond two minutes with my breath-hold, which is a sizeable improvement on my first attempts.

The next step is exposing myself to cold water. I'll admit, the breathing part fills me with energy and gives me a quietness of mind, followed by a gentle fizz in my body for the day. But the idea of dunking myself in an ice bath fills me with dread. Thing is, I have an ice bath ready and waiting for me in the form of my pool.

I don't know why, but I do two random, spur-of-the-moment things. After watching an extraordinary documentary by the Japanese scientist Dr Masaru Emoto about how water in its crystalline form reacts to positive thoughts and words to create beautiful geometric shapes under a microscope, I decide to bless my pond.

I don't know how I should do this but I garble some thoughts about what I want it to be, how much joy it will bring and the gratitude I have for getting this far. Yes, this act is definitely a little 'woo-woo', but it makes me smile, and gives me a glow of inner warmth.

Then, on this outpouring of goodwill, I decide that it's time to strip off and swim my first ever length of the pool (the swimming zone has just enough water in to make this possible).

I stand naked by the end of the pool with my bare feet on the sand just behind the sandbag wall. It's a chilly, cloudless day and I feel both strangely liberated and single-minded about this decision. I peer in and the water is so clear that I can see the Maltese cross effect of the paving just over a metre beneath me. From the corner of my eye, I notice Charlotte opening the kitchen door. She stands still, watching me. It must be a helluva strange sight, but somehow she knows it's not the time to interfere.

I'm not sure whether to jump in, dive in, or lower myself into the water. I decide for the latter. As I dip my ankle in, I take a sharp intake of breath as the cold flashes through my nervous system. But there's no going back now. I lower the rest of me in making sure I concentrate on my breath. It definitely helps. When I'm fully in, up to my neck, the cold embraces me like a jelly mould from the freezer. I'm so shocked that I yell a couple of expletives.

There is a part of my brain screaming at me not to do this, but I override this noise. I know I mustn't shiver, or chatter my teeth, so I shut my eyes and keep breathing. Then I push off. I've never been in anything so icy and my blood pumps around my body as if it is a filled with a crystalline light-filled liquid, and the chatter in my head completely stops until all I can hear is my breath.

When I reach the other end, I have a tremendous urge to pull myself out. I resist and gather myself. I take several deep breaths and push off again. This time my body has adjusted; internally I have warmed up. By the time I've swum back, I'm a little light-headed, but it's time to stop. I don't want to push the cold on my first try.

I climb over the sandbag wall and all the nerves and tissues in my body fizz like a firework and endorphins explode in my brain. I hobble around the sandy sides of the pool and let out a roar of triumph. I am euphoric.

Charlotte marches up to the pool. Her eyes are like saucers and I'm not sure if she wants to laugh or have a dig at me. She tells me I'm completely mad and adds, in a more serious voice, that I should never do this again without telling someone. What if I had frozen to death, or had a heart attack?

I give her a big, cold hug.

Thing is, perhaps what Wim and the cold are trying to teach us is how to be truly alive.

Above: the snaking land drain through the sand and cement bag wall.
Below: Tom raking out mounds of sand and gravel.

The pipes are
covered with
gravel, followed
by a garden
membrane.

A blue water pipe
runs round the
pond feeding air to
the air stone low
down in the drain
pipe which
connects to the
land-drain beneath
the sand and gravel
thus creating a
reverse Venturi
effect.

Plants and Play

I begin a regime of exercising, which isn't helped by my knees who don't want to join in. Progress is slow, but in addition to the exercises, I face going into the cold by swimming in the pond every day.

Boy, this is tough. The late winter pool temperature hovers from 6 to 10 degrees Celsius (42 to 50F). (For comparable purposes, a heated pool is about 23C or 75F.) While this isn't an ice bath (4 degrees or below at 39F) this is definitely shiver territory.

Every single time my mind screams at me not to go in, but I find the breathing exercises help to override this fear, filling me with a kind of cool bravado. I walk in up to my waist and cup water over my midriff, shoulders and the back of my neck. This method acclimatises the body and limits the cold shock. Then I push off into my curious version of breaststroke and I fix all my physical and mental energy on swimming the eighteen metres to the end and back. The cold water is crystal clear and now and then I spot newts scuttling out of my way to the bottom of the pool. When I emerge, black water beetles dive for cover under the paving slabs. It's lovely to see these new inhabitants of the pond.

Each time I emerge exhilarated that I've conquered a moment of fear. For the first time in ages, I feel intensely alive. As a result, I'm less anxious, and my mental health has a new quality of being contented and clearer. It's as if I'm receiving a natural elixir direct from the universe.

Someone points me toward a book called 'Breath' by James Nestor. It's short and fascinating and I'd highly recommend it to anyone interested in what he calls the lost art of breathing. I take many tips on board, but one major one is to breathe through one's nose. After all, that's the point of the hooter in the middle of our face.

Charlotte often accuses me of snoring (even with the goofy mouth guard in) so, as recommended in the book, I try taping my mouth up at night with a small piece of surgical tape. The effects are almost immediate. I sleep deeply, dream lucidly, and my snoring ceases. After two weeks, I abandon my mouth guard and amazingly, my teeth cease grinding. I've never used my rubbery mould again.

I can feel my Achilles tendon getting stronger. The gross fungal infection on my heel—now I am bootless—has disappeared and I'm learning how to walk again.

I don't know why, but I develop a serious case of haemorrhoids, something deeply uncomfortable and horribly relentless. It's probably a spin-off from my opiate-based constipation, or the toxicity of paracetamol trying to get out of me. So, guess what? I start a new set of medications. This new cocktail is an alluring blend of creams and enemas.

I imagined haemorrhoids were something old people suffered from. But I'm not such a spring chicken anymore—I'm nearly fifty. I'm in poor physical shape and I'm overweight, which doesn't help when it comes to exercising on knackered knees. I visit the doctor about my knee pain, but all I get is yet another prescription, a new handout and an appointment with a young, super-fit physio student called Dennis. Full recovery feels ever so far away.

The best medicine for me right now is to make sure I have my daily dip in the pond; it keeps me going, and the water seems to benefit my soul.

* * *

Before I fill up the pond from the borehole, I raid brother Charlie's garden hedge where he'd deposited a load of unwanted concrete paving. I dust off an army of ants and a million spiders and stack the slabs into my Skoda, which groans at each load. Every pothole makes me think the suspension is about to collapse.

Using these slabs, I make a pathway leading out of the pool at both ends. Then I cement the outer perimeter of the liner with thick wooden posts that I'd randomly brought down from Yorkshire.

When I revisit David's video, I realise I've forgotten to finish the overflow, even though I'd dug a trench to the old ditch-pond nearby and filled it with a plastic land-drain. It's hard to see the pond overflowing as right now water only reaches up to the sandbag wall, but an old friend arrives and after a long lunch and too much wine, we set about trying to work out where the overflow pipe-height should go. When we're done, I'm pretty sure that if the water was ever to rise this high, it will have already spilled out over the top and into the field opposite. Nevertheless, I tighten the overflow pipe socket to the liner with an 'O' shaped ring clamp and stuff the ends with balls of chicken wire.

Next, I double-check the fittings from the air blower, but find the connections don't align and air gushes out. I heat the end of the plastic pipe with a gas-powered weed-wand until the material softens, and tighten it to the blower's metallic nipple with a Jubilee clip. The plastic hardens neatly around it.

With a last check of the bubble-pump drainpipes and the air circuit connections, I take a deep breath and turn on the air blower. It's heart-in-mouth time and I punch the air as the first two bubble-pumps start bubbling away, then the third springs into life... but for some reason, all four won't work simultaneously.

Is there's a hole somewhere? Have I got something wrong?

I tease the small silicone pipes to release any blockages and adjust the height within the vertical drainpipes of each air-stone. Once again, only three out of the four bubble pumps are frothing. I double check for air bubbles in the water and when there aren't any, I have a terrible feeling I've messed up.

When Charlotte comes up to see how it's going, I try to hide my disappointment. She tells me she's fed up with the whole thing and says she doesn't want any bugs, insects, or animals in the pond. Especially rats. Rats terrify her. I don't know what to say. I try to articulate that being an organic pool it's kinda open to any creature that wants to come in. I tell her enthusiastically about the newts I've seen on my swims and she looks at me horrified, and says that this definitely wasn't part of the deal. (Was there ever a deal?)

I'm not sure the penny has dropped about what an

organic pool really means. It means water-bugs, newts, dragonflies and many birds. I can't wait to see which creatures drop in.

When I attempt to explain this to her again, she dithers and says,

"As long as nothing bites."

I can't guarantee this, but I tell her confidently that we won't have fish. She looks relieved. Fish, I continue, will pollute the water with their poop and muck up the frail ecosystem.

Then, as I shiver in the wind while drying off, she asks, "Can we heat it?"

I shake my head in disbelief. Has she paid zero attention to the process all this time? She stomps off, muttering to herself that this project is not only the biggest waste of money ever, but that she'll never swim in it. It's another low point.

After this strange year of looking after us, Charlotte needs a break. Later, we discuss taking a family holiday in the USA and her remarks are forgotten.

I'm feeling better than I have for ages, but I'm struck down by a reemergence of haemorrhoids which manifests excruciatingly moments before we take our seats at the musical Hamilton, in London. Charlotte has been looking forward to this for a year and the last thing I want to do is upset her. The entire way through it feels as if I'm sitting on a sharp flint. By the end, I'm squatting while leaning one bum cheek on the seat. It's one of the most uncomfortable evenings of my life.

At home, the bleeding intensifies. This coincides with news from an old friend, Matty, (I lived with him before we were married), who recently survived an episode of bowel cancer. When Charlotte sees the condition of the toilet bowl, she insists I call the doctor immediately. She's worried I might have something similar, a possible 'complication'. I know Matty's recent experience is at the forefront of her mind, and I put off going for a few days in the blind hope that I'll suddenly recover.

When I finally call the surgery, I can't get an appointment for several days. I know yet another course of pills and creams is on its way, but the pain is so all-encompassing I have little option.

When I turn up at the surgery, I am told there is a stand-in doctor on call.

"Is that OK?" I'm asked, as if I really have a choice.

When I open the door, the GP is a super-friendly mum from our youngest's school who I often chat to in the carpark. I had no idea she was a doctor, and I don't know what to say. I bluster about what's wrong with me in an incredibly British way.

I know they've seen it all before, but it's taken me a week to summon the courage to get here. I try to rein in my embarrassment and we dilute talking about my arsehole with chit-chat about our children and I'm grateful that she deals with me incredibly professionally. I arrive home with another course of medicines and Charlotte asks why I'm sweating. I tell her what happened, and she thinks it's hilarious.

She has referred me to the hospital for a procedure the following day, which, considering the 'wait just to see the GP', is a tremendous surprise. It sends Charlotte into a spin and she pulls out her very best nursing skill and offers me a double-whisky. I'm told the procedure is a standard practice;

a small camera inserted in the rectum to check the intestines to make sure everything is all tickety-boo.

I Google the procedure that night, which is a silly thing to do. I don't sleep. My intuition tells me my ailments are because I'm overweight, probably by three or four stones (20kg, or 40 pounds).

At the hospital a cheery middle-aged female physician, her demeanour that of a happy vicar, guides a camera up my derriere while delivering a slick, well-rehearsed, non-stop commentary, almost certainly developed to put patients at ease. After all, there's nothing like tensing up with a camera half way up your guts.

She gives me the rare compliment that my internal organs are looking extremely healthy and she points to a monitor where I see the image of a sludgy pink tube filled with red blood veins. I'm intrigued by how the camera bends around, with little or no discomfort to me at all. I ask questions about what we're looking at and she cannot wait to tell me. I'm sure we go on way past the allocated time and the discourse is surreal, especially when the camera comes out. It turns out I'm OK, but big bunches of haemorrhoids need removing.

* * *

I decide to sort my weight out once and for all. I removed sugar from my diet a few months ago, including all breakfast cereals, chocolate, fizzy drinks and puddings, but I decide to go further and drastically cut down on my alcohol consumption.

I stumble upon an unusual weight-loss book called "The Hunger Diaries" written by a writer-friend called Andrew McKay. It's an amusing, no-holds-barred narrative from someone who was horribly overweight and worked out that his health came down to a personal choice. Diets, he discovered, simply don't work. Almost by mistake, he stumbles upon fasting and at the end of his story, he leaves references to the books he studied. I order these on my Kindle and power-read them over the next couple of days.

At the end of my reading binge, it's clear to me we eat too much, and way too much junk. This boils down to the fact that we rely heavily on skewed historical food references, muddy guidelines and brilliant advertising. Now that I think of it, I've watched endless people dieting and failing—in a perpetual loop—making the diet business appear like a gigantic marketing scam.

I announce to Charlotte that I'm going to try fasting. Her immediate reaction is:

"So, now you're going to starve yourself?"

"Not at all," I reply. "It's called a water, or clean fast and mankind has been fasting for millennia. I want to see if I can do it."

She looks at me as if to say, *why can't you do anything normal?*

"Look," I say, desperately. "Right now, I'll try anything, darling. I just want to be well again."

The following week, on a deliciously warm spring evening, family friends come over to see how the pond is progressing. Without hesitating, the children pile in, loving the fresh water, diving in from the sides and throwing a ball about. It is wonderful to see the pond used for the first time and to hear the sounds of splashing and laughter resonating around the pool.

Even Charlotte understands how lovely this is and I glow inwardly as she attempts to explain to her friend how the bubble pump system works. It is a diabolical explanation, but I'm thrilled she's finally engaged. From the way she paddles in the shallows, I can see she's toying with going in.

Afterwards, I grab a mug of tea and sit quietly, watching a flight of swallows flash over and into the water as a blistering purple sunset settles over the trees in the distance. It's so still that I can hear their beating wings and the splashes of their beaks touching the water along with the gentle bubbling of the air pumps.

The planting zone has nearly a hundred tons of sand and gravel at a depth of approximately one-foot all the way around. I desperately need to fill this expansive surface area with aquatic plants. I make one list of suitable species and another of local pond owners.

To kick things off, I visit a pond at the bottom of the hill, but it's horribly overgrown and I'm wary that at least one of their plants is almost certainly on the prohibited species "invasive list".

I inform the owner, but he shrugs and tells me he's just sold the house, so he doesn't care. I leave empty-handed. The next pond I visit has endless reeds and other tall plants. It turns out that digging a plant out of a pond is far harder and messier than I expected; the root systems are extensive, thick, and horribly inter-woven.

I line the boot of the car with a plastic sheet and it's just as well. I stuff clumps of bullrushes and other reeds into an assortment of buckets until they are overflowing. By the time I'm home, it's dark, and the car stinks of pond sewage. If Charlotte goes anywhere near it, she'll go ballistic. I quietly offload and leave the doors open overnight.

In the morning, I divide the plants and place them around. I'm disheartened by the tiny area they cover. I dig holes with my bare hands in the sand and gravel until I touch the landscaping material. Then I firm in the roots. When I've completed this boot-full, I realise to my horror that I'm going to need at least another fifteen loads.

I remember David mentioning that if a pond is left for four years it will naturally fill with plants anyway. This patient approach suddenly appears more attractive, but I hate to think what the colour of the water will be in the meantime with no plants to clean it.

I have a lot of foraging to do if anyone's going to swim this summer.

It's early May and the arable fields around us shoot up in a frenzy of growing. The nepeta bank offers a first flush of lilac flowers, and fresh, shiny, lime-coloured leaves fill the trees around the ditch-pond. This also signifies that the cricket season is underway again. I'm invited to play at the beautiful cricket ground where I snapped my Achilles and on hearing this, Charlotte looks at me as if I must be insane. It's been nearly a year since the break, but I'm desperate to try, so long as I don't run. To be fair, most of the team can't run anyway, so I won't be miles off the pace.

I'm asked to bowl and realise this could be tricky. I pivot

from one foot to the other and hurl the ball as fast as I can, surprising not only myself, but the batsman who hasn't expected my Trebuchet attack method. I come through unscathed and reckon that I have passed the first small test of my rehabilitation.

At the end of the game, I take my garden designer brother, Ed, who gave me the idea for the pond, and drive through my host's meadow to his large, heavily over-grown pond. I strip off and wade in, armed with a serrated bread knife. There are so many water lilies I hardly know where to begin. When I find a suitable one, I trace the delicate stems down from the pads and flowers to gnarly tubers which sit on the bottom of the lake like thick rope knots. I quickly discover that it's easier to pull them up by hand rather than cut them out. Soon, I'm handing my increasingly bemused brother piles of bullrushes, irises, canna lilies and a mix of grasses and water-mint. At least, with its metallic peppermint smell, I think it's water-mint.

On my way home, while negotiating one of North Essex's ancient, winding lanes, a bucket tips over, leaving a grey slurry-stain on the carpet of the boot. We open the windows, but the car stinks again. Oh, my days.

After more trips to various lakes, ponds, and private streams, the planted area fills, but I'm mindful that many of these plants won't accept the measly planting medium of sand and gravel. I read about oxygenating plants and at the local garden centre I buy a single strand of pond weed.

An oxygenating plant sounds like something every pond should have, but I have absolutely no idea if it will survive. Little do I realise the havoc this one strand is going to cause.

Fast, Fetty and Silk

After supper one night, I begin my first water fast. The plan is not to eat for the next 24 hours and I think I've read enough books on the subject to know what to expect: hunger pangs will come and go in half-an-hour slots and when you sense this, the key is to drink a glass of water to fool the belly into feeling it's satisfied. I press through the day, carry on past supper, and sleep like a log.

At breakfast the following morning, I'm unexpectedly buzzing. I feel so great that I keep going and finish at lunchtime with a small salad and a boiled egg. I'm surprised at how easy it was and I have a lovely sense of energy in me, which is totally unexpected.

A few days later, I decide to go even bigger and attempt two days and two nights, and go to a third if I'm feeling up for it. As I pass the forty-eight-hour mark, there's a feeling of cleanliness, as if the natural fats in my body have taken over. I feel light, clear-headed, and energetic. When the evening meal hunger pangs arrive, I remember reading how soda water fills up the stomach and how hot water with a slice of lemon and a lick of sea-salt helps too. I pass the third day comfortably, although Charlotte is giving me strange looks and tells me my breath smells.

I'm still doing the Wim Hof breathing and cold water every morning, but my intuition tells me that a freezing swim or shower is excessive if I'm not eating. On day four, I feel sharper than I have for ages, but it's time to stop. I don't know why, but I have an urge for, of all things, a bag of crisps. So I peg off to the Pebmarsh Londis and attack a bag of barbecue flavoured hula-hoops. It's a curious ending, but I notice how I truly savour the flavour of everything I eat.

Uncle Kiff arrives from Canada and comes round to inspect the pond. He has thick, cartoon-like grey hair, and sparkly dark eyes shaded by bushy eyebrows. He's a doctor and one of those people that everyone warms to. Kiff is a bottomless source of hilarious and brilliant anecdotes, which he delivers in his gentle South African accent with a wide smile.

My fasting idea does not impress Kiff. He tells me I should be careful and I intend to be.

Over the past two or three decades, I've observed him keeping an eye on my mother's health, or rather, her infirmities. Mum's problems would have been instantly helped if, years ago, she'd changed her diet and lost weight. As children we were brought up on a classic country diet of meat and two veg, but it came with a lot of rich puddings, fizzy drinks, and sweets. This was all fine when we were endlessly running around playing football and cricket, but it doesn't translate well later in life.

Kiff is lean and fit. He bicycles, runs and hikes, eats the right things and keeps his mind active. In fact, he's a classic role model for healthy living. I'm a little surprised at his reaction to fasting, especially in lieu of the overwhelmingly positive testimonials I've read and how fasting seems to enable the body to switch to a system which heals using stored fats in a process known as autophogy. Fasting is fantastic for weight loss and is a boon for good health.

Fasting is free, but the cynic in me wonders if natural, or alternative methods of healing are sneered at because they don't follow the Pharma-centric medical model, taught at pretty well every medical school in the world, which sees profit at the end of every transaction. The problem with the Pharma-method is that some patients end up with escalating medical complications, increased pain, and a much thinner wallet. People like me, who cannot exercise and are spiralling into obesity, are the ones who slip into this dependency funnel. I can see how I'm falling headlong in, and its greasy sides are hard to claw back from.

I'm determined not to follow this route, so I'm going to trust myself and what I've experienced so far. I'm going to continue doing intermittent fasting because I really don't want to be patched up any more. Right now, the combination of this and the Wim Hof Method feels like more than just a band-aid.

For my gut problems, some kind friends gave me some kefir grains along with detailed instructions on how to make it. Kefir grains are a strange macaroni-like bacteria which you soak in milk for a couple of days to make a type of yoghurt. Who knew yoghurt made yoghurt?

Kefir is a great source of good gut bacteria. After a couple of weeks of sipping half a glass every day, I can feel the benefits rippling out to other parts of the body. Even better, the dreaded haemorrhoids have decided to leave me alone. Using kefir slots in neatly with my growing understanding of alternative healing elements to combat body toxicity, which for me has been way out of kilter.

Perhaps I need to seek more help from nature. There's plenty of information out there. I've just got to be prepared to find it.

Kiff seems genuinely enthusiastic about the pond, but he can't understand why I haven't built a jetty. He notices my unease, but outlines how simple it would be.

"All you need are the right tools," he says, far too easily.

Thing is, I tell him; I have strange thumbs, which are missing tendons (I can bend them back to a right angle). Anything I cut with a handsaw goes wonky. He grins at me. He means power-tools, and he tuts when I admit I don't have any.

We end up at the local builder's merchants ordering a pile of wood and I research chop-saws (skill saws) and circular saws. I don't admit it, but this is way out of my comfort zone.

An impressive pile of wood and a pack of carriage bolts arrives the moment he's flown home to Canada. I pick through this assortment in bewilderment, wishing I'd paid more attention to his and to David's jetty construction details. Building the jetty, which he made sound so simple, now seems rather daunting and complex.

I wander down the lane to see Tony, a thick-set man with a dense head of silver hair, a Captain Haddock beard and quizzical eyes. Tony is a master carpenter with a workshop filled with odds and ends of timber, pipe, and metal. Although he's getting on in years, I know he finds it hard to resist a challenge, so I explain my dilemma and two days later he's sorting through my woodpile and making a plan.

It turns out that Uncle Kiff was right. I have over complicated things. My jetty will have two four-metre long horizontal beams overlaid with planks, with one end bolted to posts that are cemented in by the pond's edge. We will suspend the other end over the pool using a ladder-like construction, and its base will sit on the underwater paving step.

After staining the planks a colour that claims to be 'dark oak' but looks like rust, Tony cements the anchor posts and when these set, we assemble the jetty in a couple of hours.

The jetty suits the pond with its neat simplicity. Where it meets the swimming area, Tony adds a couple of cross-bars to create a climbing ladder and screws in a handrail. I add a slightly wonky towel bar. The jetty acts like a diving platform, and everyone is thrilled with it.

Two days later we have a lovely warm day with hardly a breath of wind. It's the type of evening where you can trace the path of the first dragonflies buzzing like mini helicopters up and down the pool, occasionally drifting off to inspect the reeds and flowers. Although the pond requires more plants, the water is perfectly clear; three out of the four pumps are working, and the water level is holding.

My mounds of aggregate and building materials are nowhere to be seen. The cuckoo sings from the woods nearby and early swallows loop and barrel like mini aerobatic craft splashing into the pool to catch a drink, an insect, or to collect a glob of mud to make a nest. Even the dogs take a refreshing dip after a walk and thirstily lap up the water. And I'm feeling leaner and fitter than I have for ages.

Then, without telling me, and without fuss, Charlotte slips quietly into the pond for an evening swim.

The pool is just shy of twenty metres, and Charlotte emerges after not one but six lengths. I feel skittish.

"Any good?" I ask.

"It's like swimming in silk," she says, smiling. She has a wonderful smile.

I agree. "Refreshing?"

"Absolutely bloody perfect."

I'm dancing inside. She's right, the water does feel different. There's no chlorine, no salt, no chemicals running off the fields, just water filtered through sand and gravel. It has a velvety structure, and when you come out, you're fresh and clean all over.

After a week of regular swimming she's hooked, and the conversation quickly moves on to having some kind of structure where we can sit, change, and maybe, one day, party. I've got my eye on having a space where I can write.

There are thousands of cabin models on the internet, a few of which are within our budget, and I hobble down the lane again to Tony's barn to see if he might be interested in putting one together. Ideally, the cabin will sit opposite Kiff's jetty with a view of our house. I sketch a rough plan and add a deck and a larger jetty suspended over the pond.

The Swiss-style cabin I prefer has the unusual name of 'The Ipswich', which just happens to be the name of the football team I fervently support. Charlotte opts for one called the 'The Newcastle'. I suspect she's only gone for that one because that's where she went to university. The Newcastle is too big so we look again and the only other one with the correct dimensions is 'The Leeds', which, she claims, is her football team (a boyfriend took her to a game when she was seventeen). I'd bet money she doesn't know what colours they wear, but it's a cabin toss-up between Ipswich and Leeds.

Tony's face lights up when he sees the sort of thing I've got in mind and his brain slips into overdrive. In moments, he's worked out that he'll need to suspend the cabin on a deck, which means digging a huge number of holes into the old farmyard concrete and tarmac under the thin veil of so-called soil. I let slip that it might be harder than he imagines. He shrugs it off.

"Wood rots quicker if it's laid on concrete," he tells me in his muffling Suffolk burr. "And if the building is in line with the top of the pond, it'll be the right height to jump off."

It's a neat observation because, to avoid any exterior water running in, the pond is higher than its surrounding area.

Charlotte is wary about building the chalet on a platform, but I tell her that the wind passing underneath the cabin will discourage rats.

No rats or snakes wins every time. It seals the deal.

Above: Pumps are in place. The bund with tiny nepeta plants!
Below: The pool fills up in the Spring heatwave, and the kids pile in

C (above) explaining how she thinks the pond works
My first plants by Kiffy's jetty.

Above: Kiff's jetty and below: Tony, having a tea break in the heat.

The Fountain of Youth

Hugo, an old friend, arrives to stay and thanks me for introducing him to the Wim Hof Method. I'm delighted he's taken it on board, and I ask him how it's going.

"Epic," he says. "I now lie in a freezing river once or twice a week near Stroud with a bunch of mates."

The following day, with his wife and son, and in blazing May sunshine, we wander down the lane past fragrant apple blossom, busy birds and the fresh green shoots of barley to my parents for a barbecue.

Staying there is my twin brother, Ed, and his daughters. We spark the Braai into life and soon red-hot coals are cooking a mountain of food. Everyone bathes in the sunshine and salivates at the delicious smells. We tuck into the first bottle of Provence rosé of the year.

I'm not the only one happy Hugo has embraced the Wim Hof method. Our kids (mine and Ed's) have never come across anyone who's practiced Wim's breathing and cold before, and in one quick move I'm not such a freak.

The three of us (Ed has started Wim Hof too) do a couple of rounds of breathing, which are widely snickered at. Hugo asks the kids if they've ever tried it. They haven't, and we can see them squirming as if this is some kind of voodoo freak show.

I challenge my thirteen-year-old son, who rates himself as an athlete, to some press-ups. I tell him I'll do mine withholding air. They look at me as if I'm mad. Buoyed by this challenge, I make thirty fast, deep breaths and then, releasing all the air, I start my press-ups without breathing again.

My son gets to about fifteen, but I'm still going strong at twenty before running out of reserves five later when I take my recovery breath. Everyone is gobsmacked. Recently, I could barely walk, was almost obese and now I'm cruising through press ups with no air in my lungs. It's a breath-hold technique I'd picked up on Wim's app and it feels terrific.

Hugo tells me that in return for showing him Wim Hof, he has a routine for me that should sort out my tight hamstrings. The story goes that in the mid-1800s, a stooped old gentleman with a cane, Colonel Bradford (possibly a pseudonym), went in search of the Lamas (Tibetan monks) who had discovered a "fountain of youth".

To the astonishment of his fellow officers, he reappeared four years later, lean, strong, and fit. What happened?

The colonel explained that he'd stayed with the Lamas high up in the Himalayas. Every day they practise a stretching/meditation/breathing exercise or routine known as the Five Tibetan Rites. These Rites are over 2,500 years old and strengthen the spine and thereon-in all the connected tendons, like the Achilles, hamstrings, and neck, while enhancing one's metabolism, cardiovascular function, energy levels, and balance. In short, it boosts all the vital energy centres in the body. According to Colonel Bradford, the "Five Tibetans" will help you stay healthy, energised, youthful, and vibrant.

My flexibility is dreadful. I haven't been close to touching my ankles for about three decades. These are perfect exercises for me.

In the sunshine, Hugo runs through them.

The first involves spinning clockwise on the spot with ones arms outstretched. When you stop, you plant your legs, take two deep breaths with your eyes open, and overcome the spin. It's best to start with three, building up with an additional two every week until you reach 21. Over time, so say the Tibetans, this improves one's balance and will prevent you from falling when you're old.

The second is a kind of stomach crunch, but with straight legs, the third stretches the spine backwards from a kneeling position with your hands on your buttocks. The fourth is a swing from a sitting position up to a bridge and back to a sitting position again, and the fifth pivots from a cobra position up to a downward dog. (Find out more at the end of the book).

There's much hilarity when we try them, especially the first rite, which involves spinning. One daughter whirls dramatically into the swimming pool. And with the 'moving into a bridge' exercise, half of us can't do a single one.

The following day, I find a video of the Five Tibetan Rites to make sure I'm attempting these stretches correctly. What I hadn't realised is there's an emphasis on inhaling at the start of the stretch and exhaling as one returns to the original position.

I do the Five Tibetan Rites every morning. I begin with three repetitions of each, and increase this by two every week.

After ten weeks, I'm up to the maximum of 21 repetitions. These simple exercises are exactly what I need and what better place to do this than beside my pond.

In a couple of months, my tight hamstrings are no longer like overstretched guitar strings and for the first time in living memory I can easily touch my toes.

Other benefits are that my posture has improved, and my body, or more accurately, my back, is way more comfortable after a day of sitting and typing at my keyboard. I feel leaner, with more energy and my sleep is deeper than ever.

Aside from the benefits of stretching the body, it's obvious the rites are stimulating important areas like the thyroid gland. And there is such a lovely calmness when doing these exercises. It's not a competition, or something you need to "push through" to achieve. To me, it is a meditation and a breathing exercise, as well as a stretch. The whole routine takes fifteen to twenty minutes, depending on the gap I allow between each repetition.

The very next day, I am quietly running through the Five Tibetan Rites by the pool when my eyes are diverted by the shadow of a huge wingspan going over the pond. A buzzard glides over my head and settles on Kiff's jetty.

I stop and stare at this impressive bird as it eyes me back.

I'd like to think it's giving me some encouragement to keep going.

Father and Son

It's turning out to be a glorious summer. The days are hot and dry, and in the long, warm evenings we have endless barbecues until we're sick of sausages and burgers. My spartan pool is in constant use and the water is wonderfully refreshing.

Tony brings in a pile of solid oak posts in his transit van. These will support the deck, which will cradle "The Ipswich". He's had them in storage for years, he tells me with immense pride, exactly for moments like this.

At one foot deep, Tony's spade clunks into the footings of the old barn and farmyard. I can't tell if it's the heat or the exertion of trying to bash through the foundations, but Tony's pulling a good sweat already. It's probably both.

Realising that he will almost certainly hit this layer of brick and cement across the footprint of the cabin, Tony changes tack. His logic goes something like this: if these are the footings of the old barn, then its floor will act as a foundation as long as there are more holes. So, instead of digging twelve deep holes, he's going for twenty-four shallower ones. This is a lot of spade-work.

Meanwhile, I'm back playing cricket again for the mighty Bures. In the afternoon sunshine after a long tea, we amble out and take our places in the field. The bowler is about to bowl the first ball when the skipper notices we haven't got a wicket-keeper. After many jokes and the usual wise-cracks he asks,

"Does anyone know how to wicket-keep?"

I raise my arm. I'd tried it years ago and loved it. Besides, if I can't run what better use of my legs than to stay put and catch the ball?

This arrangement works well. From just a couple of weeks of regular stretching, and having lost weight (two stones, or approx. 13kg - from 15 stone to 13 stone), I am decidedly more agile. I reckon I can bend my knees enough to cover the necessary ground. Fortunately, my reactions are still intact and my performance is decent enough to seal the wicket-keeper spot for the next few games.

I'm batting with a 'runner' (this is a player who runs my runs—if you remember from earlier—when you receive an injury during the game, a law that is generously overlooked for me at our level of play) but I get run out almost every innings because of a godawful mix-up between me, the runner and the other batsman. On this occasion it's a very family affair, with my elder brother, Charlie, and my nephew George, and a horrendous lack of communication.

Despite this inconvenience, it's fantastic to be playing again, and I managed to club a few balls into the nettles by the river, which is enormously satisfying.

* * *

My new weekend chore is to raid ponds and dig out water-lilies and irises. These two varieties have struggled to push their roots into the nutrient-light medium of sand and gravel, whereas the bullrushes and grasses are expanding rapidly across the planted zone.

With my scarcity of plants, the heat, and plenty of use, I really need all the bubble pumps to work correctly. The pond is greening-up with a thin, streaky-green algae and blanket weed. I'm worried that if this carries on, I'll have to halt all swimming until we get a break in the weather.

I revisit David's notes about the bubble pump and even though I'm sure I assembled each one exactly as he directed, I can't understand why they don't seem to operate together. My air blower hums like an electric milk float, and when I take the clip off I get a face full of air, so the pump isn't faulty. I investigate the connections between the blue water-pipe (that makes up the air circuit) and double-check these intersections. Being underwater, leaking air would bubble to the surface; I find nothing.

And then I realise what the problem is. My circular air pipe is thicker than David's. I check my notes. His air pipe was 12.5mm in diameter, mine is 20mm. I don't know whether to laugh or cry. All that is required is a greater volume of air.

I purchase a new air-blower, pull out my gas-fired weed-wand and heat a three-way plastic connector onto which I cram the ends of the pipes. I tighten jubilee clips on the warm, soft plastic and offer a small prayer. When the plastic cools, I turn the two blowers on. In each corner, all four bubble pumps gurgle before bursting into life, the flow noticeably stronger. This is how it should be.

Within a few days, the algae has largely cleared.

* * *

The following week, I finish my second long fast. After two days, I couldn't see the point of stopping, so I carry on, drinking water and keeping busy and centred for further two days, about 110 hours in total.

I don't think fasting would be enjoyable, or indeed, possible, if it's done simply to lose weight. There's a great deal more to it mentally. Fasting is an exercise in discovering inner peace. It's a way of connecting to a higher part of oneself, something I've discovered that meditation develops.

Each element of breath-work, fasting, and stretching complements the other perfectly. And now I'm sensing a change in awareness of my natural self and how my body and my mind are responding, or rather, opening up, to this new way of doing things. For the first time, I'm understanding the inner me and how my body and mind work.

I don't know if this is how one finds one's spirit, but I realise how important it is to really nurture one's mental and physical wellbeing. In that respect, I've taken a great leap forward in understanding this soul of mine. And I'd like to think that this new me is emerging from out of the pond.

A euphoric sense of well-being fills me after completing this fast. Once again, I'm astonished at my energy levels and every part of me feels lively and fresh. Soon afterwards, I'm tucking in to another bag of Hula Hoops (don't ask), salad and slices of salami, nuts and cheese, and I truly relish every mouthful.

To combat the ever-expanding blanket weed, I dream up a horrible-looking contraption; a jumble of pipes with odd-shaped connectors, metal rods, and lock-ties with an air-stone neatly nestled in the middle, which connects via a long thin pipe back to the air blower. My plan is to stir up the heavily oxygenated water stuck in the bottom of the pool.

I lower this curious pastiche into the middle of the pond and a stream of bubbles rises to the surface. I don't know if this will work; it's the lack of established plants combined with the long heat wave, which is the real problem.

With thick algae surrounding the plants, I spend a couple of afternoons fishing out the sloppy mush with a long net and an assortment of garden rakes. It is impossible to remove algae in a hurry, so this exercise reminds me of Tai-Chi, the movements deliberate, flowing, and patient. A long afternoon session feels like extensive mind and body therapy.

* * *

None of my clothes fit. Rather than buy a whole new wardrobe (I might slap on the pounds at a later date) I drop into the cobblers in town and have all my belts re-holed. At home, when I check the scales, the battery has run out. The thing is I feel comfortable and content in my body. I don't need scales and I don't want to be measured any more. I just want to be the best version of myself at any one time.

After explaining this reasoning to Charlotte, I toss the scales in the rubbish bin. There's an element of joy in doing this; perhaps it's my tiny kick in the teeth to the dieting industry.

We head off to a wedding and for the first time in over

twenty years, I slip into the trousers I wore at our wedding. It feels great.

* * *

Tony's struggling in the heat. He's a barrel-like unit and nearing seventy years of age. I tell him he's more than welcome to take a dip in the pond. He looks at me as if I'm deranged. His son, Jamie, arrives to help and we discuss the jetty. Jamie has long jet-black curly hair, a chiselled jawline, dark eyes, and a rakish scar on his cheek. Even with his dark-glasses on, it looks as if he's just walked off the set of Pirates of the Caribbean.

Jamie is a metalworker, metallurgist and metal-tinkerer, and, like his father, he has the practicality and prowess to turn his hand to pretty well anything. I sketch out the type of design I've got in mind for a larger jetty in front of the Ipswich. Jamie and Tony get it straight away, coming up with neat alterations and nifty suggestions.

Jamie says he can source some metal barn rafters for the frame, which he'll add to an order at another job he's working on. Tony reckons he can source some decent decking. I make a decision that we might as well get on with both the deck and the jetty, especially while Jamie has a couple of weeks off and the weather looks set to remain fine.

A day before our long-awaited family holiday to the US, something we all need after such a turbulent year, and almost exactly a year since I snapped my Achilles, the Ipswich cabin turns up in the belly of a vast lorry. Behind the plastic curtains and wrapped in tight, white cling-film are the timbers which, I hope, Tony will piece together like Lego while we're away.

The stocky, shaven-headed Estonian lorry driver reverses down the old track, the scowl on his face at having to negotiate our dreadful Essex lanes clear in any language. He refuses a cup of tea, a rare event, marches to the rear of his enormous truck and leaps onto the attached three-wheeler forklift and begins, with surprising dexterity, to pull the cabin slowly out. It's nail-biting watching him move the long, heavy timber package that wobbles like a glider's wings in turbulence, and only on completion does the grunting Eastern European allow himself a trace of a smile.

We'll be back in three weeks, I tell father and son. Tony assures me it'll all be done by then, but over a third of the posts still need to be dug, and in this heat, hole-boring is energy sapping. As this is going to be my new writing den, or, poshly, scriptorium, I'm going to need it the moment I get back.

Trying to imagine what it's going to look like fills me with nerves. I have images in my head which veer from a luxurious Swiss ski-chalet, to a reception hut at a car-boot-sale. The further we travel towards Heathrow, the more anxious I get, but there's nothing I can do about it now.

I've been practicing the Wim Hof Method nearly every day for six months and I understand why so many people are trying it. Of course, some people can't see past the cliché that it's just a *breathing and getting incredibly cold* fad.

In reality, it's far from the fast-fix world of well-intentioned post-Christmas gym membership sign ups, which are not only expensive but where visitations tend to fall off a cliff after a fortnight. Wim's method is free and anyone can do it at home. It's simply breathing, cold, and meditation.

One helps the other to stimulate feeling alive—but this doesn't happen overnight and it requires dedication. If you put in the work, boy, it's worth it.

When people ask why I do it, the honest answer is that it benefits me, physically and spiritually. It's a quick-fire route into meditation, and I didn't know what that was until a few months ago.

When I breathe, I imagine sucking a bright light into every part of me, especially my midriff, my heart, and my head. When I quieten the chattering part of the brain, I travel in my mind through my body to every ache and pain, especially my knees, which I spray down with an imaginary internal pain-quenching-spray, like a mini fire-hydrant.

This method really works (losing weight helps too) and for the first time in a decade I don't have a constant nagging knee-pain. What a difference this makes in my life.

Soon, I notice a change in my breath retention, which comes at the end of my round of forty deep breaths. According to Wim on his many YouTube videos, this is where you "go deep".

I didn't know what "going deep" meant. I think it's a method of connecting to one's inner being and how we quieten the monkey-chattering side of our brain, which is so dominant in our everyday lives.

It turns out the "going deep" process is wonderfully calming. For a long time in these breath holds, I'd use a stopwatch, hoping like mad I could get to two, maybe two and a half minutes, three if I was lucky.

But it's on our last day of our American vacation in San Diego when we find a vast sandy beach that I truly get it.

Foamy, rolling waves casually unfurl over flat sands. Couples sit about chatting while others play ball games in the warm evening sunshine. Swimmers bob in the water, their heads like pins, waiting for waves to bring them home on the surf. In the background, the giant orange dome sends long shadows across the sand. The scene is nothing short of idyllic.

While the kids enjoy the surf, I do three rounds of breathing. On the breath-hold, I am so relaxed that I pass three minutes, then four, then five. It's effortless. I've "gone really deep". It's as if I'd entered a trance-like state, where the body slows down so much that you slip into a kind of wondrous daydream.

Since then, I've removed the stopwatch and trusted myself.

On reflection, I appreciate I've come a long way. It's now several weeks since I've taken a paracetamol. This stuns me because I took at least four paracetamol every day for the best part of five years, mainly for my creaking knees. And while my knees still don't function properly and I walk with a slight limp, at least they don't hurt.

My gut is better. My ankle is strong. My torso is leaner and my posture has improved and those grinding teeth are a thing of the past. I sleep like a baby.

As the kids ride the surf in this glorious sunset, their laughter decorating the sound of waves rolling over the sand, I cannot think of a better end to a brilliant holiday.

Now, I cannot wait to see what Tony has done while we've been away.

* * *

We arrive back home at dusk. The first thing I do is look through the kitchen windows towards the pond. I can't disguise my frustration.

"You thought it would be up, didn't you?" Charlotte says.

I nod and worry that something has happened to Tony. It's late, so we head to bed. I have a restless night but I'm deeply relieved to see Tony driving in the next morning wearing the same black, smeared-in-paint-'n-glue T-shirt that we left him in three weeks ago.

He fills me in. It turns out that after excavating twenty-four holes into the concrete and then cementing-in his oak posts, he needed a break from the sun. Thank goodness he's OK.

The positive news is that the deck—on which the chalet will live—and the additional deck towards the pool are done. And Jamie has finally (after continuous chasing by his dad) welded the metal frame for the jetty.

This jetty is a three-dimensional "T" shape. The main section will sit above the pond with the bottom bar resting on the paving ledge three feet below in the pool. The leg of the "T" is a walkway which will match up to the main deck. It's a clever piece of design by Jamie and probably drafted on a cigarette paper.

I'm concerned that the significant weight of the metal on the paving above the liner might force a stone through the membrane, or, worse, a sharp corner might catch and tear the liner. Tony's face lights up, he's got just the thing. He'll strap sections of incredibly tough fibrous cushioning to the bottom of the metal beam. He's had the stuff for years, he tells me, with the look of a man who absolutely knew that his sheets of strange material would one day come in handy.

We now have to lever the entire unit into place. The problem is that this structure is way too heavy to manhandle. It's the one thing we haven't thought of.

I ring Chris—the farmer with the blond hair—and explain our problem. He has a lad in a field nearby lifting voluminous round bales of straw onto a long trailer. He wonders whether this would work. Fifteen minutes later, a green John Deere front-loader, a curious-looking machine which appears a little squashed on one side but with a long, telescopic arm, runs up the garden to the pond.

With the help of a couple of straps, the entire metallic structure rises into the air, looking like a small section of a roller coaster. The lad operating the loader stretches the prongs to the absolute limit, just far enough over the pond, and begins to lower the unit. None of us, bar Jamie, can bear to watch.

It's a great show of control and skill. He doesn't drop, bash, or destroy the walls, dent the decking, crush the plants or puncture the liner. Then he drops the structure to Jamie, who stands, half-submerged in the pond, wearing his jeans and dark glasses.

Jamie fixes the bolts and the jetty slots perfectly into place. While Jamie ties the remaining sections together, Tony joins the thinner end neatly to the main decking area. The wooden slats marry up to the existing deck perfectly. We're all relieved. Charlotte can't believe how smart it looks, nor can I. We celebrate with a round of cold beers.

Jamie has a look on his face which tells of a quiet satisfaction, and he gives his dad a look as if to say, "I bloody told you, mate".

Above: Levering the jetty into place using the telehandler, and left, me foraging for plants in the pond at Rockalls.

The bund is filled with Nepeta Six Hills Giant creating a wonderful flush of colour over the summer months.

Roof shingles being attached to the 'Ipswich' log cabin

Cabin and Cold

As Tony predicted, the piecing together of the 'Ipswich' takes a couple of days; slotting on the roof shingles another. It's brilliant watching them work it out, fixing the beams together like a gigantic puzzle. In no time, the pallets of cedar have morphed into a building which looks like it should belong halfway up a mountain. It even has that distinct fresh alpine smell, just like a sauna.

The cabin feels vast as all empty rooms do, but I'm envisioning it as part office, part changing room. Charlotte has other ideas. We'll need to agree about what the chalet should be. (I'm currently typing this in the chalet, so for the time being, I have the best office in the world.)

Tony tells me I need to apply at least two coats of paint to the entire building to preserve the timbers. I knew this was coming and I know it'll take two or three days. Thing is, I'm miles behind on my work. Then Tony reminds me that this includes painting the inside, 'to trap the sap in the wood'. Let's call it a week.

We now enter a colour conundrum. The chalet sits at the

end of our garden in full view of the house and the garden. Having spent hours painting small tester squares onto every wall, we invariably choose the colour we originally thought of. It's a grey-green 'Barn' paint, curiously called 'Forest Green', and, much to our relief, it works perfectly.

Charlotte finds an off-cut from the local carpet store and when the man delivers it, I spend an hour of his time explaining how the pond works. I think he's entertained by my enthusiastic rambling, but the occasional glazing-over of his eyes suggests he doesn't have a clue what I'm talking about. After he leaves, I make a horrible mess of installing the carpet with a jumble of bent nails. I should have asked for some carpet stretchers, but hindsight's a wonderful thing.

A week later and the last part of having a fully operational chalet arrives. Ricky, a mouse-like young man, arrives to quote on wiring the chalet. His vehicle is a spotlessly clean white Ford Escort van which gives away that he's recently started his own electrical business. I ask him when he can start.

He's doing a full house re-wire nearby, and he's booked up for the next three weeks.

"Three weeks! Oh..." I say, disappointment in my voice.

"But... I can come round after hours... if that's not inconvenient."

I stop short of hugging him and jump at his generous offer. When he arrives a day later, I realise I have completely misjudged the number of lights and electric points. Ricky scribbles in pencil where further sockets and fittings should be.

Ricky is as good as his word and for the next few evenings, and often well into the night, he wraps cables in and around the cabin and I can hear the whirr of his drill from the house as he fixes away.

When he's done, soft spotlights spill a gentle light over the deck, which illuminates the foliage of the bullrushes swaying in the wind.

Inside, I put up some curtains, load up an old bookcase, install my desk and stock up a large wooden chest with colourful swimwear and beach towels. On the walls I add a myriad of family pictures and random canvases of animals.

It looks a bit of jumble and Charlotte insists she's going to change things around, but my most precious gift is the glorious view across the pool. Its beauty is not complex, rather a simple reminder of how wonderful nature is. And every day it reminds me of my healing journey.

I'm installed and I can't quite believe it.

A health routine is emerging. (See *My Healing Guide* for more.)

For one or more days a week, I do an intermittent fast. This means that I skip breakfast (16/8) or I enjoy one meal a day (a 24hr fast). Sometimes, I extend this to 48 or more hours.

Every morning I do a breathing routine on my deck (not just Wim Hof breathing, there are a plethora of breathing exercises out there), followed by a cold shower or a few lengths of the pool, occasionally swimming to the side to see how the plants are coming on, or to pull something out, or to check the bubble pumps.

I do my Five Tibetan Rites in either the morning after a cold shower, or after a swim, or in the evening on the deck over the pond. It's here where I feel closest to nature and the heavens above.

I still dread the idea of going in the cold, but every single time I do, I'm happy I did because it defeats a large portion of fear. We humans are over-burdened by fears of all types and badly equipped to let it go. A great way of releasing fear is to get into the cold. It forces us out of our comfort zone and helps us appreciate we are stronger than we imagine. These days, if I have a cold shower, and our borehole water is super-cold, I sing at the top of my voice—usually a dreadful operatic mash-up. This is incredibly annoying to everyone in the household, but I love it. It makes me feel reinvigorated.

As a result, I'm enjoying the sensation of being leaner and fitter than I've been for years. My energy levels have changed too, and I'm much more aware of what I eat, and how I approach thing like gratitude, positivity, and intention. I've metamorphosed from a fat, juicy caterpillar into a butterfly.

In summer, the shallow, planted surface of the pool warms up quickly and the pool can reach a balmy 80F or 26C. When this happens, I hook up an outdoor shower from the borehole to get my cold fix. Later in the year, with the first frosts, the pool temperature plummets. This is when swimming requires real mental firmness. You're on your own and there's no one who can help you.

As autumn approaches, I'm contemplating swimming all year round. Swimming through the autumn months is the way to acclimatise to these colder temperatures. When the temperature dips to 14C (about 58F), I feel the bite. Below 12C (the yearly average North Sea temperature) it's getting super-chilly (Fun fact, the North Sea rarely dips below 7C or 45F).

Although you know you'll feel great at the end of it, actually experiencing the cold is a tussle of the mind and a blast to the body. I don't know if I have the testicular fortitude to swim every day of the year, but I'm up for trying. It's not the cold water that really gets you, it's the biting wind that pervades into one's bones.

It's when you exit the pool in a winter gale that you really know about the cold, when your blood pumps slower and your skin turns a curious colour of blue. After a session like this, I return to my cabin, dry myself off, sip on a hot mug of tea, slip a woolly hat on my head and jump around. Often, a long walk with the dogs is an excellent way of warming up.

I'll only dive in if the temperature is above 14C as you can experience brain-shock if it's too cold, which can be dangerous. Below this, as I mentioned earlier, my method of entering the pool is to wade in by the side of the jetty and splash my hips, neck, and shoulders. It's now almost a ritual, the moment when I've passed the point of no return; I am committing myself to do something completely contrary to my brain's best intention.

When I'm in the cold water, with controlled breathing, I concentrate solely on the first few strokes. Chattering and shivering will not help you one bit. Panicking is a disaster and a mindset that may well plunge you into a hypothermic state.

After a minute or two, the body warms up. It's a fabulous, surreal feeling, as if God has wrapped you in his hand. Anyone who's ever taken a dip in the sea will have experienced this strange change to the body. There's a natural heating system in each of us and you have to trust it will activate.

When the pond is near freezing, it is ice-bath territory. I'll walk in the shallows to the end of the jetty and lower my torso in, keeping my head out. I concentrate on my breathing and almost instantly, the cold knocks all my thoughts away. Time stands still. The water prickles over one, feeling adversely, hot—until you don't really feel the water at all.

What about hypothermia? I had a mild brush with hypothermia once after getting carried away in the icy pool in the middle of winter. I meant to do three or four minutes, but my brain emptied and my breathing was so controlled that I ended up in a trance-like state for eleven minutes. These days I let Charlotte know if I'm going in so she can keep half an eye that I get out safely.

If you're interested in trying the benefits of cold, but the idea fills you with horror, why not try a five-second cold-blast after a hot shower extending the cold duration every day. Just remember to breathe deeply and not to fret.

* * *

A few days later and it's been a fresh, chilly but bright autumn day. I spend several hours typing at my desk in between looking out of my window over the brown, ploughed field, warmed by a small electric fire. That night, when I'm done, I turn off the lights and walk out onto the jetty. A full moon hovers from behind the house and reflects in the water, the four corners rippling, the reeds swaying. It's a breath-taking scene.

Looking back on the past year, I can't help but think how momentous it has been for all of us. I am a changed person. I've grown as a human being, touching on aspects I would never have dreamed of a year ago. I've done things *my* way, and it's worked. I have learned to take responsibility for my health and it feels incredibly liberating.

From the blandness of a derelict farmyard and its mountain of rubble, I have a pond that is not only a glorious oasis of nature but, amazingly, actually works. It has echoed my personal journey. My bashed-up body is fitter and pain-free, and I have tuned-in to the healing power of Mother Earth. It's been hard work and an education laced with setbacks, but I have discovered a whole new way of doing things.

My journey with my healing pond has made me emerge a little more polished as a human being, definitely more knowing, and certainly more trusting, of my place in the universe.

It's been worth every minute.

And best of all, Charlotte loves it too.

Below: A late evening summer swimming party

Above, family enjoying a dip.   Below: Sunbathing on the jetty

I receive a lovely award at the end of the 2021 cricket season.

I forgot to mention it. The dogs love the pond too.

What happened next?

I always maintained that if anything went drastically wrong, it would still be a simple pond. The wildlife alone would be worth the effort; deer, buzzards, swallows, geese, dragonflies, water bugs and newts among countless other visitors—some encouraged more than others.

FIVE YEARS ON FROM MY POND BUILD, HOW HAS IT ALL GONE?

Not everything went according to plan...

Complete sections of the sandbag wall collapsed into the swimming zone. It turns out I hadn't blended the correct mix to create concrete, so when the hessian bags rotted, sand and cement slipped down the sides to the bottom of the pool.

This precipitated a sudden boost of vegetative activity from that single piece of the 'oxygenating' plant I threw in—the pond weed, remember? This solitary slither of weed embraced the alkalinity of the cement like flies on dung and multiplied all over the bottom of the pool. (Charlotte called them the "Bloody Trees!") In a pleasing twist, these plants kept the water amazingly clear while the other plants were getting established.

A year later, it took two days to dredge the pond weed with a rake I constructed from cricket-net poles. Thankfully, the pond has since stabilised. In the grand scheme of things, the effect of the walls disintegrating isn't drastic. Bullrushes now grow right up to the edge, which lends its own charm. One day, I might repair the edges, but as I said, it's only a pond, not the Sistine Chapel.

My homemade, strange-looking bubble contraption I threw into the middle of the pond to stir up the heavily oxygenated water at the bottom came up in the dredging. I don't think it was necessarily a good idea, but it was great fun making it.

During one particularly violent winter's storm, the roof shingles on the chalet disappeared into the valley. I've patched the roof up twice. A more robust roof is on its way.

In extended warm periods, algae reappears, but I discovered some friendly bacteria which works wonders and gobbles it up. It is brilliant stuff.

Some things went better than expected:

Simon, who built the second block wall around the swimming area, did a stunning job of rebuilding the patio by the house, not me. But... when we realised the pond was more lovely than we had dared to dream, I dug into a section of the spoil-mound and levelled this area out for sun lounging.

This gave me the chance to prove my fitness. I erected a pergola and laid a patio using terracotta Mediterranean tiles.

And it wouldn't be complete without a bar I made from pallets. The area has a lovely rustic feel and climbing plants will soon cover the pergola. It is a wonderful place for summer lounging, barbecues and drinks.

If you're wondering, yes, it is all still standing.

Clearing the reeds by hand in late Autumn
Below: The new pergola area

And me, personally?

I haven't taken a single pharmaceutical product for four

years; not even paracetamol, not even for a hangover! I am rarely, if ever, sick.

I continue to do breathing exercises, the Five Tibetan Rites, and cold water almost every day. I do intermittent fasting each week and a longer fast twice a year.

On reflection, I wish it hadn't taken so many broken joints to make me change my ways. I should have done all of this years ago, but I simply didn't know how.

At the mighty Bures Cricket Club, I was given the Chairman's Award in 2021 and the Batting Cup in 2022. While this isn't exactly Sports Personality of the Year, it meant a great deal to me. Knees permitting, I no longer try to use a runner.

From being a pond which we thought we might swim in for those steaming, breathless couple of weeks, we now swim daily. Charlotte swims for at least six months of the year. I swim for eight months, intermittently over winter—though obligatory on Christmas Day—and for the occasional ice-bath!

Charlotte told me at the end of last year that building the pond was the best thing we've ever done.

My Healing Guide

My practices and more information:

Important note: None of the following constitutes medical advice.

What works for me may not work for you. Listen to your body. If you are in any doubt, always seek professional help and **always do your own research**.

BREATHWORK AND THE WIM HOF METHOD

The Wim Hof Method is a simple process that requires a regular dedication of 20 to 40 minutes daily, in order to extract the benefits.

Initially, I followed Wim on the Wim Hof Method app, but there are loads of breathing instructors on YouTube who use 'breathing bubbles', or musical, or linear timers. They follow roughly the same principles of powerful in-breathing followed by a breath-hold or breath retention.

There are a wide variety of breathing techniques to check out when you're a little more confident.

Do NOT do the following while in water, or while operating machinery, or on an escalator, or when flying an aircraft. (I shouldn't have to say this, but there's always one...)

Basic Method:

Lie on your back or sit with back straight and do approximately 30-40 deep breaths repetitively (and I do mean deep, so that you actually move your diaphragm). Breathe in through the nose or mouth (whichever is more comfortable) and out through the mouth, but don't exhale all the way out.

On your final breath, release all the air, and simply hold the air out without breathing in again.

It is completely counterproductive to tense your body. Try to relax by visualising the various body parts in your mind as you go.

For example: Relax your cheekbones, eyes, eyelids, ears, relax your chin, jaw and neck. Release the shoulders, let out your tummy, etc. See the body parts in your mind's eye as you run through them.

After several seconds, you'll feel an urge to breathe. Try to resist the gag constrain on your throat and override this sensation. (It's really hard at first, but very doable.) What you're doing is controlling your fight-or-flight mechanism.

Then, when you really, really have to breathe, suck in a huge breath and hold this right in for ten-seconds squeezing your loins and pushing the air from your sphincter up your back and into your head.

Then release. Take a couple of recovery breaths and repeat the cycle again.

At the end of the third cycle, take a little time to reflect. This is a great time to offer gratitude and positive affirmations.

You don't have to stop at three, but three will give you a lovely natural high and leave you in a positive state of mind.

THE FIVE TIBETAN RITES (OR THE FOUNTAIN OF YOUTH)

Top and bottom: My daily Five Tibetans. (Parts one and two.)

Practicing the Five Tibetan Rites is not a competition, so go easy on yourself and don't rush. The 5T's are a combination of a stretch, a meditation and a breathing exercise all in one. They have a stimulating effect on the energy systems of one's body. **There is no need for over-exertion**.

Check out my YouTube channel for a full demonstration of the Five Tibetan rites.

Begin with just three rounds of each rite per day for the first week.

Then add two per week so that by week ten, you should be up to 21 repetitions. This is the starting method recommended by Colonel Bradford. Many changes take place in the body and you don't want to be unbalanced, moody or become nauseous by hurrying on to the maximum of 21 repetitions.

The 'gifts' of the Five Tibetan Rites will come during this build-up time.

Practice the Five Tibetans before bed or early in the morning on an empty stomach. Beginners should do either morning or evening. Accomplished practitioners can do both.

Rite 1 - The Spin

"I am full of energy."

1. Stand with your feet shoulder-width apart. Stretch your arms wide, in line with your shoulders, and keep your palms facing down.

2. Spin in a clockwise direction, keeping your arms level and your breathing steady. Concentrate on your right thumb, or the floor, and avoid tilting your head forward.

3. Start with 3 spins, then add two the following weeks

increase to 21 spins. When you've mastered 21, try spinning 33 times.

There is no need to go fast; choose a comfortable speed that doesn't compromise your balance. On completion, take a deep breath, bring your hands together up to your chin, and fix your eyes on a particular spot. Then conquer your focus and imagine you are sending anchors into the ground via the soles of your feet.

With practice, spinning gets easier. As with any exercise, listen to your body.

The moment you feel dizzy, stop - before you fly out of control.

Spinning not only aligns one's chakras (energy centres in the body), but the benefits to your balance are immense. So much so that, according to the Tibetans, this simple exercise will help prevent falls in old age. (My batting in cricket has benefitted enormously.)

Rite 2 - The Leg Raise

"My mind is clear and calm."

Lie on your back with straight legs fixed together, arms by your sides, palms down.

1. As you deeply inhale, engage your core and gently raise both legs together while simultaneously lifting your head and rolling your chin to your chest. Keep your shoulders on the floor and your palms on the ground with fingers together.

2. Hold for a moment, then, on a slowly exhale, reverse the movement by lowering your head and legs, keeping the legs straight, and return to the original position.

3. Repeat, as per the above instructions, up to 21 times. Focus the breath on an energy centre in your body (the

abdomen area, the heart area, or a point between the eyes) and link each movement to the inhale and exhale of your breath. This is a great eye exercise too, focussing on far away points at the top and bottom of your lens range, to close up on your chest.

Note: this exercise engages your core. Avoid if you are pregnant, if you've had recent abdominal surgery, or a spinal injury. If it is too difficult, change the posture by placing your hands under your buttocks, or bend your knees as you lift and lower your legs.

Rite 3 - The Kneeling Backbend

"I am flexible and receptive."

The third rite is a dynamic version of the yoga posture known as 'camel pose'. It's a pleasant exercise to do with your eyes closed.

1. Kneel with your hips over your knees. If you have knee pain, place a folded blanket under them. Keep your back straight and place your chin towards your chest.

2. Place your hands flat against the side of your legs. On the inhale, lean back, pushing your chest out and arching your spine. As you move, slide your hands down your legs. At the same time, tilt your head back as far as you can go, squeezing your shoulder blades together to increase the stretch. Check how your spine feels and do not lean too far back for the first few times. Your toes should prevent you from falling backwards.

3. As you exhale, go back to the original kneeling position, straightening the spine and bring your head forward so that your chin rests on your chest.

4. Relax for a moment, then repeat, as per the instruc-

tions above, up to 21 times. When comfortable and with no muscular irritations, try bending forward first before you lean back. This exercise strengthens the back muscles.

Note: With all backbends, it's essential to keep your core engaged by pulling the belly button inwards as you lean back. This will protect the lower back and prevent injury.

Rite 4 - The Tabletop

"I am strong and balanced."

The fourth Tibetan rite also requires core engagement. This one strengthens the abdominals, upper body, and upper legs.

1. In a sitting position with your legs straight and a shoulder width apart, place your hands by your sides with your palms flat on the floor. Tuck your chin into your chest.

2. Inhale, pressing your hands into the floor and lifting your hips, swinging them forward by bending your knees. (Your hips should swing up in line with your body so your knees are over your ankles and your shoulders are directly over your wrists).

3. Now you're in a front-up tabletop position, or bridge. If you can, lever your neck backwards. Hold this position for a moment.

4. On the exhale, gradually lower your hips by swinging them back to the seated position you started in, ending with your chin on your chest. Relax for a minute.

Then repeat, as per the instructions above, up to 21 times.

Note: As this exercise requires arm strength, you can start with bent knees until you build up strength in your upper body.

Rite 5 - The Pendulum

"I am positive and motivated."

This last rite is also known as *the two dogs*, or *the pendulum*. It features two common poses, the downward-facing dog (where your head is pointing at the floor) and upward-facing dog (where your groin is pushing into the ground and your back and head arch upwards).

> Notes Colonel Bradford. *"If one is very heavy, he should be cautious in using No.5 until his weight has been greatly reduced."*

1. Start in either pose, but most people find it easier to begin in an upward-facing dog. Lie on your front and push up with your hands so your shoulders are directly over your hands. Keeping your arms straight, push your chest out and tilt your head back. With a deep inhale, pivot...

2. ... tuck your toes in while extending your hips back and up. Straighten your legs. Extend your arms and push your chest back towards your thighs. You will now be in an upside-down "V" shape, or "downward dog". Hold this position for a moment.

3. Exhaling, bring your weight forward and back into the upward-facing dog once again. Your hips should sink down so your arms are aligned with your shoulders, which are over your wrists. Your legs should be off the floor, supported by your toes. Keep your chin up as you press your chest forwards and tilt your head back.

4. As you inhale, return to the downward dog by lifting the hips up and back.

Then repeat, as per the instructions above, up to 21 times.

Note: As you raise the body, breathe in deeply, then exhale fully as you lower your body. Do this rite as one smooth motion at a relaxed pace. Rest between each movement as needed.

Colonel Bradford: *"All five rites are of importance. Even though he may not be able to perform them the prescribed number of times, the individual may rest assured that just a few times each day will be of benefit."*
"These Rites are so powerful that if one were left out entirely while the other four were practiced regularly the full number of times, only the finest kind of results would be experienced. The First Rite alone will do wonders... so if anyone finds that they simply cannot perform all five of these Rites, or that they cannot perform them all the full number of times, they may know that good results may still be experienced."

After performing the Five Tibetan Rites, enjoy a tepid, or cool shower or bath. But **never** take a cold shower, cold bath or use a cold wet towel which has the capability of chilling you. This will undo all the good you have gained from performing the Rites.

Recommended reading: The Eye of Revelation, the true five Tibetan Rites, by Peter Kelder & Carolinda Witt.

FASTING

Fasting, or Intermittent Fasting is a practice which will help clean your system and will aid you in discovering your spiritual self. It will probably not work, or be easy, if you are doing this only to lose weight. Fasting needs to be done with an understanding of what is at stake in terms of MIND and BODY.

If you're serious about giving this a try, **I strongly recommend reading the following books:*

The Complete Guide to Fasting - Jason Fung MD

The Transformational Power of Fasting - Stephen Harrod Buhner

(The Hunger Diaries - Andrew MacKay)

What Is Intermittent Fasting (IF)?

Intermittent fasting is an eating pattern that cycles between periods of not eating (fasting) and time allocated for eating.

It doesn't specify which foods you should eat, merely when, or the timings, of your next meal. Think of it as more like an eating pattern.

Common intermittent fasting methods involve daily 16-hour fasts (no eating) with 8-hours where you eat. Putting this in simple terms, it means missing breakfast from supper the previous night and starting eating again at lunch. Easy, right?

An 18-hour fast might look like missing breakfast and lunch and having a nibble in the afternoon, while fasting for 24 hours is one meal a day. Do this twice per week and your life could change significantly.

Humans have practiced fasting for millennia, and it is an ancient part of human evolution. With this in mind, fasting from time to time is perhaps more natural than repeatedly eating 3 or more meals per day. It gives one's gut a well-earned rest and breaks the "habit" of mealtimes.

Fasting for religious reasons is well documented and occurs in almost every religion and is one key to achieving higher spiritual awareness.

Intermittent Fasting (IF) Methods

All the methods involve splitting the day, or the week, into eating and fasting periods.

During the fasting periods, eat nothing and drink only pure water. This is also known as a "clean" fast.

Some people try a fruit fast to begin with, which involves eating only fruit for a specific time.

The most popular methods of IF:

The 16/8 method: As mentioned previously, this involves skipping breakfast and restricting your daily eating period to 8 hours, such as 1–9 p.m. Then you fast for 16 hours in between.

Eat-Stop-Eat: This involves fasting for 24 hours, once or twice a week, for example, by not eating from dinner one day until dinner the next day.

Many people find the 16/8 method the simplest, most sustainable and easiest to stick to.

From here, when IF feels more natural, try a 48-hour, and then, when you feel confident, a full one-week fast for a total body cleanse. I've found that the magic really happens after 48 hours, but please make sure you read the books (listed above), so you thoroughly understand what you're doing.

And if in any kind of doubt, seek professional advice.

How Fasting Affects Your Cells and Hormones

Please do your own research.

Below are examples of some (not all) of the things that happen in your body at a cellular and molecular level. For example, how your body adjusts its hormone levels to access stored body fats. Your cells also start important repair processes and change the expression of genes.

Here are some changes that occur in your body when you fast:

Human Growth Hormone (HGH): The levels of growth hormones skyrocket, increasing as much as 5-fold. This has many benefits, but mainly fat loss and muscle gain.
Insulin: Insulin sensitivity improves and levels of insulin drop dramatically. Insulin prevents access to stored body fat so a low insulin level makes stored body fat more accessible.
Cellular repair: When fasted, your cells start a cellular repair process. This includes autophagy, where cells digest and remove old and dysfunctional proteins that build up inside cells.
Gene expression: There are changes in the function of genes related to longevity and protection against disease.

Health Benefits

Studies on intermittent fasting, in both animals and humans, show it has powerful benefits for weight control and the health of your body and brain. It may even help you live longer.

Again, please do your own research

Major health benefits of intermittent fasting are:

Weight loss: As mentioned above, intermittent fasting can help you lose weight and belly fat, without having to consciously restrict calories. https://www.frontiersin.org/articles/10.3389/fnut.2022.871682/full
Insulin resistance: Intermittent fasting can reduce insulin resistance, lowering blood sugar by 3–6% and fasting insulin levels by 20–31%, which should protect against type 2 diabetes. https://www.ncbi.nlm.nih.gov/pmc/articles/PMC8970877/
Inflammation: Some studies show reductions in markers of inflammation, a key driver of many chronic diseases https://www.healthline.com/health-news/fasting-can-help-ease-inflammation-in-the-body
Heart health: Intermittent fasting may reduce "bad" LDL cholesterol, blood triglycerides, inflammatory markers, blood sugar and insulin resistance — all risk factors for heart disease. https://www.heart.org/en/news/2019/11/25/regular-fasting-could-lead-to-longer-healthier-life
Cancer: Studies suggest that intermittent fasting may prevent cancer. https://www.medicalnewstoday.com/articles/324169#boosting-the-immune-system-to-fight-cancer
Brain health: Intermittent fasting increases the brain hormone BDNF and may aid the growth of new nerve cells. It may also protect against Alzheimer's disease. https://www.

brightfocus.org/alzheimers/article/biohacking-brain-health-research-exploring-fasting-and-diet-changes-shows-promise#:
Anti-aging: Intermittent fasting can extend one's lifespan. Studies showed that fasted rats lived 36–83% longer. https://www.hsph.harvard.edu/news/press-releases/molecular-mechanism-behind-health-benefits-of-dietary-restriction-identified/

Many questions have yet to be answered, but let's not forget, humans have been fasting for thousands of years, most likely for a very good reason.

Next Steps...

If you would like to initiate some easy steps to kick off a fresh and fearless life without sickness, then join me on a simple healing journey for your body and spirit.

I cannot take responsibility for your health but I can try and help you make the first moves towards a fresh way of looking at things.

If you're interested in detoxifying and cleaning up your body and mind in a no-fuss and incredibly simple way, I've expanded my life-changing process into an ebook.

Here, I discuss **breathwork, fasting and stretching** but inside I include a list of remedies and practices that I've come across over the past five years.

Everyone is different. Each one of us will have a different pathway and a need for different things. There is no one size fits all.

This **starter guide** will get you on the road to finding

what those elements are and then realising your true human potential.

In my ebook/pdf :

- Why are we so sick?

- Breathwork and why it is so important.

- Fear, and how it affects you.

- I take a deeper dive into fasting.

- More stretching ideas to go with the Five Tibetans.

- Tapping (EFT), and other simple healing methods.

- How the body energy centres of the body work— your energy vortexes or Chakras.

- Meditation, and other thoughts on developing your spiritual self.

- I'll show you how to make Kefir and Kombucha, Miracle Mineral Solution and CDS.

If you've purchased this book I'd like to offer you 50% off. (*Please use:* JEHealing *at the checkout.*) Click here or visit:

www.jameserith.com/thehealingpond to register your interest.

A Personal Perspective

A FINAL WORD:

Look around. Look at the astonishing amount of people who are always sick. Look at their medications, their diets, their relationship with toxins. Look at the effect on the NHS and the days lost to work. Look at the explosion in autism, diabetes, and mental health.

Common sense alone suggests that something is wrong. The way people manage their bodies feels as if we are now accustomed to dealing with the effects of illness, rather than the cause.

This is not new. The debate of Germ Theory vs Terrain Theory (both are still *theories*) raged in the 1890s and beyond. Perhaps it is time to revisit this old battleground because it is here where today's system of medicine was borne. Modern Western society followed Germ Theory (NOT Terrain theory) and, for me, this is one big reason for our woeful general health today.

In the shadow of Emile Pasteur's success of making Germ

Theory 'de rigour', John D Rockerfeller's turned his attention to medicine understanding that this 'interpretation' of sickness paved the way for a whole industry using singular treatments for specific ailments. Hence, we see the birth of Pharma.

To fully succeed, he quashed traditional, natural healing practices known for centuries, financed medical student bodies underpinning these schools with a new understanding of pharmaceutical products, and bought the scientists and the media. Easy when you know how!

This pincer move led to our bondage to pharmaceutical interests ever since. He understood that a profitable health business relied upon sick patients and the outsourcing of ones health. All opposition was swept away. Money became more important than healthy outcomes, and the has process snowballed to where we are today with diabolical levels of ill-health in what are supposed to be 'advanced' nations.

(Check out: Rockerfeller Medicine Men, by E. Richard Brown, University of California Press 1979)

There has to be a better way.

It has drawn me towards the burgeoning natural health

movement. There's a ton of information is available online and, even better, it's virtually free. Importantly, I've learnt that some of the old ways of looking after oneself really are the best; fresh air, clean water, sunshine, exercise, and a balanced diet.

I now avoid (and it isn't possible all the time) sugar, processed foods, seed oils and wheat. I steer clear of toxic-based liquids like shampoos and suncreams, noxious sprays and fluoridated water (https://fluoridealert.org/articles/50-reasons/)

Finding balance in my life means I am better equipped to deal with toxins and trauma. Five years later, and I am rarely ever sick.

Those twins of ailments, toxins and traumas are at the heart of illness. And, right now, the toxicity around us has never been so evident. It's in processed food and drink, in the poisonous air constantly sprayed over us, in the continuing use of deadly Glysophate sprayed on our soils which permeates the land, damaging our food and leeching into our fluoride-filled drinking water.

People are waking up that these dreadful combinations are catastrophic to human health.

Every body has an extraordinary capacity to heal itself. If we can let our bodies get on with this amazing process by taking responsibility for our environment; what we breathe, drink, eat, and by unburdening our fear, we will be a lot less sick.

And if millions move to this model, then collectively, we will leave a less toxic planet behind when we depart.

God bless, and good luck on your journey.

James

So many people are tied into this book who need mentioning. My thanks to my brother Ed, the garden design genius at GardenEye, for suggesting to dig a pond in the first place, to Paddy Ford for helping me work out how to make a right angle, to David Pagan-Butler, the genius behind the pond concept and to Dave Cowlin who is a digger legend.

Then there's Simon Palmer, who rebuilt the block wall, Marty and his crew, Gary Reed and Tom Wasteney for stepping in when I really needed it, and to the brilliant Tony and Jamie Leech for their remarkable skills in both metalwork and carpentry departments.

My fabulous uncle, Dr Christopher Muller who suggested the jetty and made me toy with woodwork (not going well), and of course, my amazing parents, Robert and Sara, for being there for me with unassailable love and help. Thank you.

Thanks to my other brother, super-talented Charlie, for allowing me to steal paving from his hedge and for his great help and skill in editing this book. (The 'Trebuchet' bowling style is one of his many little gems.) Others who help me shape this tome with sharp observations and valuable suggestions are Jo Lambton, Christie Simson and Belinda Drew.

A special mention to Guy Brooks for all the plants I thinned from his pond, and for hosting so many splendid games of cricket at Rockalls. Thanks to all at Bures Cricket Club, the friendliest cricket club in the known universe, who are so supportive and patient even to players who aren't holding a beer. And thanks to all my 'runners', even if/when you ran me out.

To this day, I'm not sure how I persuaded my fantastic wife, Charlotte, to build the pond. She is and has been extraordinarily patient with all my quirks and broken parts, holding everything together with humour, sharp critique, a lot of smirks and incredibly loud laughs. The fact she's the No.1 fan of the pool says it all. Thanks, hun.

It was Charlotte who commissioned the painting for my 50th birthday, which adorns the cover of this book, painted by artist Polly Shillington, who captured the essence of the pond perfectly.

As a last word, I'd like to wish anyone who's middle-aged and who snaps their Achilles tendon my sincere best wishes. It's a vile injury and a real awakener to one's body condition. It's an ailment that takes a great deal to come back from, but you will. And I bet you'll come back fitter too. I salute you all.

Dedicated to Charlotte.

Also by James Erith

Click this link to join my Author List

TIME STAMP

A time-travel romantic thriller

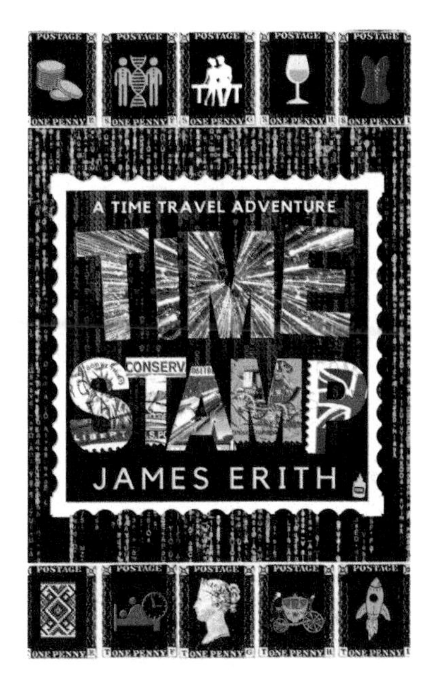

Paperback ISBN - 978-1910134528

Hardback ISBN - 978-1910134535

2058. Earth is ruled by the Elite. The boundaries between reality and artificial intelligence have disappeared. Freedom is an illusion to all but the minority who manage the countryside.

Bert Chalmers, a brilliant programmer, has been central to the creation of this new world. But he is shaken out of his complacency by a ruthless attack on a new and alluring friend, Nina.

As the Elites set out to coerce the remaining free humans into the hive-mind of the Singularity, Nina disappears.

Outraged, Bert plots an extraordinary journey back in time to secretly disrupt the past to a point where humanity started to go wrong. He's aiming to travel back at the dawn of the technological revolution in the 1990s.

But when he lands, it's the humble postage stamp which is the biggest tech around...

"....all the hallmarks of a great novel, intrigue, edginess, memorable characters, twists, a great plot, plus a touch of romance." Amazon.co.uk

FIND IT HERE:

https://books2read.com/timestamp

Or for a signed paperback (UK only) www.jameserith.com/time-stamp

EDEN CHRONICLES: FANTASY ADVENTURE SERIES

Archie, Daisy, and Isabella set out on a mission to solve three riddles and locate the sacred stone tablets that contain the key to freeing the world from an ancient prophecy.

A bestselling, family-friendly fantasy series set in the sweeping hills and ancient monuments of North Yorkshire, UK. (11+)

"What a story. It's full of life and strife, it'll make you laugh and bring tears to your eyes. Come and get lost in James's world for awhile, you won't regret it." (Amazon.com)

TRUTH—Eden Chronicles Prequel—A novella. (ISBN: 978-1910134313)

Power & Fury—Eden Chronicles, Book One (ISBN: 978-1-910134-50-4) The Power and The Fury, narrated by Rory Barnett, is now available in audiobook.

Spider Web Powder—Eden Chronicles, Book Two (ISBN: 978-1-910134-39-9) (Now available on Audiobook)

Blabisterberry Jelly—Eden Chronicles, Book Three (ISBN: 978-1-910134-22-1)

The Dragon's Game—Eden Chronicles, Book Four (ISBN: 978-1910134245)

The Eyes of Cain—Eden Chronicles, Book Five (ISBN: 978-1-910134-34-4)

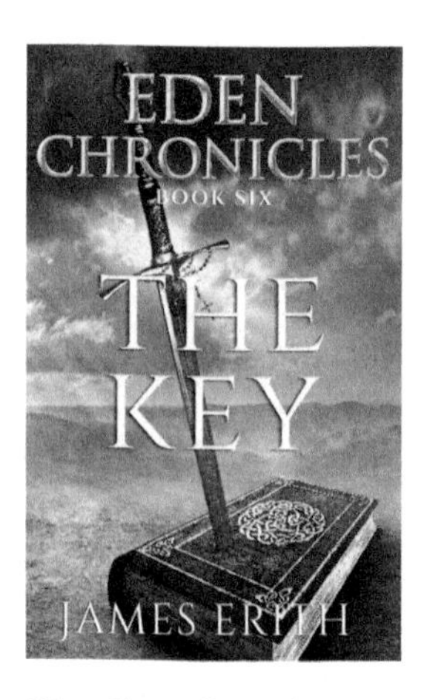

The Key—Eden Chronicles, Book Six (ISBN: 978-1-910134-42-9)

Eden Chronicles Collection 1—Books 1, 2 3 (ISBN: 978-1-910134-17-7)

Eden Chronicles Collection 2—Books 4, 5, 6 (ISBN: 978-1-910134-32-0)

About James

James at a recent book talk
james@jericopress.com

Restless after schooling, James traveled and experienced plenty of adventures. He has been shot at, scaled the great Pyramid at Giza, climbed mountains, been through earthquakes, police detained and swum with beavers.

James specialised in getting lost, like in the Canadian

wilderness in cubbing season, or in the heat of the Australian outback, as well as experiencing hypothermia, dysentery, muggings, altitude sickness, thefts, a broken neck, desert breakdowns, and so much more.

Inadvertently these experiences set James up for a big writing journey.

In the 1990s James worked as a journalist for the financial pages of the Yorkshire Post scooping the infamous Gerald Ratner "Crap" story, before upping sticks—and career—to design gardens in London.

James then moved to a small village between the Dales and the Moors of North Yorkshire. Here, the inspirational landscapes of bleak hills, old monasteries, and expansive views became the ideal setting for his Eden Chronicles series, which James began in 2007 after a nasty bang on the head.

Following a rather embarrassing appearance on ITV's, "Honeymoons from Hell" TV show (fleeing a psychotic safari operator) James was briefly an extremely minor celebrity. Fortunately, this happened pre-YouTube!

As a youth, James had his sights set on playing the game of cricket for England, but a long list of injuries and a genuine lack of talent forced the issue. However, a notable sporting triumph in 2013 saw James row the English Channel and the 21 tidal miles of the Thames in aid of MND and Breakthrough Breast cancer.

James retains his childhood passion for making dens, pitching fires, and stargazing. And he's now a bit of a health freak who loves cold swimming and looking after himself.

* * *

Swing by my Author Facebook page - James Erith Author - and give it a like, and if you're on Telegram, come and find me at Time Stamp: https://t.me/timestamp2058

For news, giveaways, freebies and other good stuff go to www.jameserith.com and join my Author List. You'll be the first to know about my new releases, audiobooks, movies etc...

www.jameserith.com

james@jericopress.com

Printed in Great Britain
by Amazon